FUNCTIONAL ANALYSIS

AND

TIME OPTIMAL CONTROL

This is Volume 56 in
MATHEMATICS IN SCIENCE AND ENGINEERING
A series of monographs and textbooks
Edited by RICHARD BELLMAN, *University of Southern California*

A complete list of the books in this series appears at the end of this volume.

FUNCTIONAL ANALYSIS
AND
TIME OPTIMAL CONTROL

HENRY HERMES

Department of Mathematics
University of Colorado
Boulder, Colorado

JOSEPH P. LASALLE

Division of Applied Mathematics
Brown University
Providence, Rhode Island

ACADEMIC PRESS New York and London 1969

ACADEMIC PRESS, INC.
111 Fifth Avenue, New York, New York 10003

United Kingdom Edition published by
ACADEMIC PRESS, INC. (LONDON) LTD.
Berkeley Square House, London W.1

LIBRARY OF CONGRESS CATALOG CARD NUMBER: 69-18354
AMS 1968 Subject Classifications 9340, 4690

PRINTED IN THE UNITED STATES OF AMERICA

PREFACE

By the middle of this century automatic control engineering was well advanced. Sophisticated analytic techniques were available for the design of linear servomechanisms and with great justification Norbert Wiener said: "The present age is as truly the age of servomechanisms as the 19th Century was the age of the steam engine ...." Kolmogoroff and Wiener had developed a mathematical theory of optimal filtering and prediction, and engineers were already beginning to consider problems in optimal control. It then happened in 1953 under the influence of Lefschetz that Bushaw gave a mathematical solution of a simple optimal control problem. This was the beginning of the development of a theory which is the subject of this monograph and the beginning of the development of a more general theory of optimal control.

Bushaw's methods for solving his special problem could not be generalized but it was his work that brought optimal control theory to the attention of mathematicians in this country and the Soviet Union. Different approaches to the study of a general linear time optimal problem were given by Bellman and LaSalle in the United States and by Gamkrelidze and Krasovskii in the Soviet Union. This led eventually to the development of a general theory and to Pontryagin's maximum principle. Many other people too numerous to name here have contributed to this problem and the theory is today quite complete. The linear time optimal problem is the optimal control problem about which we know the most and is the best introduction to the general theory.

The purpose of this monograph is to present the main features of that theory as an application of mathematics. Part I is the mathematics and is a concise but self-contained presentation of those aspects of functional analysis needed for the control problem. It includes also a few basic results from the theory of linear differential equations.

Part II is the application to the linear time optimal control problem. The two parts can be studied independently but are meant for the reader who wants both. Someone primarily interested in mathematics with an application might begin with Part I. The reader mainly interested in the basic introductory problem in optimal control theory from which the general theory arises should begin with Part II and refer from time to time to Part I. Part III is a brief discussion of the nonlinear time optimal control problem.

The authors wish, in particular, to thank their Polish friend, Czeslaw Olech, who read the manuscript carefully and made a number of valuable technical suggestions for improvement. The first-mentioned author would like to acknowledge the ideas and insight gained from numerous discussions with George W. Haynes.

March, 1969   HENRY HERMES
                                         JOSEPH P. LaSALLE

CONTENTS

PART III

NONLINEAR TIME OPTIMAL CONTROL

PART I

FUNCTIONAL ANALYSIS

1. Logical Foundations

A *partially ordered system* is a set $\mathscr{P}$ together with a binary operation $\leq$, defined between some elements of $\mathscr{P}$, which satisfies: (1) $a \leq b$ and $b \leq c$ implies $a \leq c$; (2) $a \leq a$; (3) $a \leq b$ and $b \leq a$ implies $a = b$. If $\mathscr{P}$ is partially ordered and Q is a subset of $\mathscr{P}$ such that $a, b \in Q$ implies either $a \leq b$ or $b \leq a$ then Q is said to be *completely* (*totally*) *ordered*.

If $\mathscr{P}$ is partially ordered and $S \subset \mathscr{P}$, an element $m \in \mathscr{P}$ such that $a \leq m$ for all $a \in S$ is said to be an *upper bound* of S. An element $m \in \mathscr{P}$ is maximal if $a \in \mathscr{P}$ and $m \leq a$ implies $m = a$.

Zorn's Lemma. Let $\mathscr{P}$ be a nonempty partially ordered set with the property that every completely ordered subset has an upper bound in $\mathscr{P}$. Then $\mathscr{P}$ contains at least one maximal element.

Zorn's lemma is equivalent to the axiom of choice and hence can itself be looked upon as an axiom. If the reader finds this axiom hard to accept, perhaps he may find more palatable the equivalent *axiom of choice* which can be stated as follows. *Given a family of nonempty sets* $\{S_\alpha ; \alpha \in A\}$ *with A an arbitrary index set, one can choose an element from each set* S_α *to form a new set S.*

2. Topological Considerations

Algebraic structures are described in terms of properties of exactness whose statements involve only a finite number of elements of a set. For instance, the statement of the commutative law of addition involves two elements. In analysis the number of elements involved in the description of convergence, continuity, etc., which are properties dealing with "nearness" or "approximation," is no longer finite, and it has been found convenient to base these concepts on collections of subsets called "topologies."

1

From an axiomatic viewpoint, a *topology* $\mathcal{T}$ for a set X is a family of subsets of X satisfying:

(a) the union of any collection of sets in $\mathcal{T}$ is again a set in $\mathcal{T}$;

(b) the intersection of a finite collection of sets of $\mathcal{T}$ is a set in $\mathcal{T}$;

(c) X itself, and the empty set $\varnothing$, belong to $\mathcal{T}$.

The sets of $\mathcal{T}$ are called *open sets* and the set X with topology $\mathcal{T}$ is called a *topological space*. *Closed sets* are defined as the complements of open sets. Any open set which contains a point x is called a *neighborhood of x.*

If we have two topologies $\mathcal{T}_1$ and $\mathcal{T}_2$ for a set X, the topology $\mathcal{T}_1$ is said to be *weaker* than the topology $\mathcal{T}_2$ if $\mathcal{T}_1 \subset \mathcal{T}_2$; i.e., if every open set of $\mathcal{T}_1$ is an open set in $\mathcal{T}_2$. Equivalently, in this case $\mathcal{T}_2$ is said to be *stronger* than $\mathcal{T}_1$. The stronger topology contains more open sets. Two topologies are the *same* or *equivalent* if $\mathcal{T}_1 = \mathcal{T}_2$; i.e., if they have the same open sets. This can be shown to be equivalent to: $\mathcal{T}_1$ and $\mathcal{T}_2$ are the *same* if given any open set $\mathcal{O}$ in either, and point $x \in \mathcal{O}$, there is an open $\mathcal{O}'$ in the other containing x and contained in $\mathcal{O}$.

Let X and Y be topological spaces and f a function with domain X and range in Y. Then f is *continuous* at a point $x_0 \in X$ if to each neighborhood V of $f(x_0)$ in Y there is a neighborhood U of x_0 in X such that $f(U) \subset V$. This is equivalent to the property that the preimage of an open set in Y be open in X; i.e., for $\mathcal{O}$ open in $Y, f^{-1}(\mathcal{O}) = \{x; f(x) \in \mathcal{O}\}$ is open in X. A sequence $\{x_n\} = \{x_1, x_2, \ldots, x_n, \ldots\}$ of points x_n in X is said to *converge to x* (written $x_n \to x$ or $\lim x_n = x$) if each neighborhood of x contains all but a finite number of points of $\{x_n\}$.

Let X be a topological space with topology $\mathcal{T}$ and S be a subset of X. Then we can define a topology for S to be sets of the form $\mathcal{O} \cap S$, $\mathcal{O} \in \mathcal{T}$. This is called the *relative topology of S* induced by the topology $\mathcal{T}$ of X.

If X is a topological space and S a subset of X, a family $\mathcal{F}$ of open sets in X is said to be an *open covering* of S if every point of S belongs to at least one element in $\mathcal{F}$. S is *compact* if every open covering of S includes a finite subfamily which covers S. S is *sequentially compact* if every sequence in S has a subsequence which converges to a point of S. S is *conditionally sequentially compact* if every sequence in S has a subsequence which converges to a point of X.

A family of subsets of a set X has the *finite intersection property* if every finite subfamily has a nonempty intersection. Using this, one easily gets the following characterization of compactness. *A subset S of a topological space X is compact if and only if every family of relatively closed subsets of S with the finite intersection property has a nonempty intersection.*

If X is a topological space with the property that each pair of distinct points of X has disjoint neighborhoods, the topology is said to be a *Hausdorff* topology.

EXERCISE 2.1. Show that a closed subset of a compact space is compact.

3. Ways of Generating a Topology

Let X be any set. From the axioms it follows that the collection of all subsets of X is a topology for X; it is called the *discrete topology* and is the strongest topology. From the viewpoint of analysis it has little value, since with this topology each point is a neighborhood of itself and this eliminates approximation. On the other extreme is the weakest topology for X, called the *indiscrete* topology, which consists of the two sets $\emptyset$ (the empty set) and X. It again is quite useless in analysis.

Our next task is to consider ways of generating significant topologies "between" these two extremes.

Let X be a topological space with topology $\mathcal{T}$. A *base* for the topology $\mathcal{T}$ is a collection of open subsets $\mathcal{B}$ of X such that any element of $\mathcal{T}$ can be written as a union of elements of $\mathcal{B}$. Let X be a set and $\mathcal{B}$ a nonempty collection of subsets of X which satisfy: (i) For each $x \in X$ there is a $B_x \in \mathcal{B}$ such that $x \in \mathcal{B}_x$. (ii) Given two sets $B_1, B_2 \in \mathcal{B}$, if $x \in B_1 \cap B_2$ there is a $B_3 \in \mathcal{B}$ such that $x \in B_3 \subset B_1 \cap B_2$. We may then define the elements of a topology $\mathcal{T}$ for X to consist of arbitrary unions of elements of $\mathcal{B}$ together with $\emptyset$. It is easily seen that the axioms of a topology are satisfied, and $\mathcal{T}$ will have $\mathcal{B}$ as base.

A nonempty collection S of open subsets of a topological space X is called a *subbase* if the collection of all finite intersections of elements of S is a base for $\mathcal{T}$. Let X be an arbitrary set and S a collection of subsets of X. Then there are certainly topologies for X which contain S (for instance the discrete topology), and there is a unique topology for X containing S, which is weaker than any other topology with this property. Indeed, since the intersection of an arbitrary collection $\{\mathcal{T}_\alpha\}$ of topologies of X is itself a topology, take the intersection of all topologies containing S. It will be the weakest topology containing S and as such is unique.

A more constructive way to characterize the unique weakest topology containing S is by taking all unions of finite intersections of elements of S, together with $\varnothing$ and X, as a topology for X. This is the desired topology. It has S as a subbase.

As an example, which will be useful later, let X be any set and let Y be a topological space with topology $\mathcal{T}(Y)$ and $\{f_\alpha; \alpha \in A\}$ a collection of functions, each defined on X with range in Y. The *weak topology generated by* $\{f_\alpha; \alpha \in A\}$ is the weakest topology in X under which each of the functions f_α is continuous. This requires that $f_\alpha^{-1}(\mathcal{O})$ be an open set in X for each $\alpha \in A$, $\mathcal{O} \in \mathcal{T}(Y)$. Let $S = \{f_\alpha^{-1}(\mathcal{O}); \alpha \in A,$ $\mathcal{O} \in \mathcal{T}(Y)\}$ and use S, as in the previous paragraph, to generate a topology. This topology with S as subbase is then the weak topology generated by $\{f_\alpha\}$.

PRODUCT TOPOLOGIES

Let $X_1, \ldots, X_n$ be topological spaces, with $\mathcal{B}_i$ a basis for the topology of X_i. Their *topological* product $X_1 \times X_2 \times \cdots \times X_n$ is defined as the set of all n-tuples $(x_1, \ldots, x_n)$ with $x_i \in X_i$, taking as a base for the topology all products $U_1 \times \cdots \times U_n$ of U_i in $\mathcal{B}_i$.

The *product* $X = \prod_{\alpha \in A} X_\alpha$ of an arbitrary family of spaces $\{X_\alpha\}_{\alpha \in A}$ is defined as the set of all functions x with domain A and range $\bigcup_{\alpha \in A} X_\alpha$ such that $x(\alpha) \in X_\alpha$. When the X_α are toplogical spaces a topology is assigned to $X = \prod_{\alpha \in A} X_\alpha$ by taking as a base the sets consisting of products of nonempty open sets U_α with U_α in X_α and $U_\alpha = X_\alpha$ for all but a finite number of α. With this topology $X = \prod_{\alpha \in A} X_\alpha$ is called the *topological product* of the spaces X_α. For each $\alpha \in A$ the mapping P_α defined by $P_\alpha(x) = x(\alpha)$ is called the projection of X onto X_α. The product topology above can then be seen to be the weak topology generated by the family of projections $\{P_\alpha; \alpha \in A\}$. An important property of topological products, which we state without proof, is:

Theorem 3.1 (Tychonoff). The topological product of compact spaces is compact.

Another very useful way of generating a topology for a set X is via a *metric function*, which is a real-valued function ρ defined on pairs of elements of X satisfying: (1) $\rho(x, y) = \rho(y, x)$; (2) $\rho(x, z) \leq \rho(x, y) + \rho(y, z)$; (3) $\rho(x, y) = 0$ if and only if $x = y$. It follows that the values of ρ are greater than or equal to zero. A set X with a metric ρ considered as a topological space with base defined by the " open balls " $\{y; \rho(y, x) < r\}$, $x \in X$, $r > 0$, is called a *metric space*. Any set X may be made into a metric space by defining $\rho(x, y)$ to be zero if $x = y$ and one if $x \neq y$. This yields the discrete topology and is trivial. However, an important question is: given a set S with a topology $\mathscr{T}$, can one determine if $\mathscr{T}$ is a metric topology; i.e., can a base for the elements of $\mathscr{T}$ be defined via a metric function? If this is possible the topology is said to be *metrizable*, if not it is *nonmetrizable*. (Necessary and sufficient conditions for a topology to be metrizable can be given.)

In a metric space X, compactness and sequential compactness of a set S are equivalent.

A sequence $\{x_n\}$ in a metric space is called a *Cauchy sequence* if for every $\varepsilon > 0$ there is a positive integer N such that $\rho(x_n, x_m) < \varepsilon$ whenever $n, m \geq N$. A metric space is *complete* if every Cauchy sequence converges to an element of the space.

EXERCISE 3.1. Let K be the set of all nonempty compact subsets $A, B, \ldots$ of n-dimensional Euclidean space E^n. For $x \in E^n$ the *distance* $d(x, A)$ *of* x *from* A is defined by $d(x, A) = \min\{\|x - a\|; a \in A\}$ and define

$$2\rho(A, B) = \max_{a \in A} d(a, B) + \max_{b \in B} d(b, A).$$

Show that ρ is a metric function for K. (This is called the *Hausdorff metric* for K.) If $\|a - b\| \leq c$ for all $a \in A$ and all $b \in B$, show that $\rho(A, B) \leq c$. (Here $\|x\|$ denotes the Euclidean length of $x \in E^n$.)

4. Linear Topological Spaces

We shall assume the definition and basic concepts of a linear space X over a field Φ are known. The elements of X are called "points" or "vectors" and the elements of Φ are called "scalars." If X is a linear space and if S is a subset of X, *the span of S* is the subspace of X consisting of all finite linear combinations of elements of S. A subspace S has *codimension one* if it is not the whole space and if there exists one element $x \in X$ such that the span of $S \cup \{x\}$ is all of X. A *hyperplane* is any translation of a subspace of codimension one. A *linear functional* on X is a scalar-valued linear function defined on X. Note the following result.

Lemma 4.1   A subset H of a linear space X is a hyperplane if and only if there is a nontrivial linear functional x' on X and a scalar c such that $H = \{x; x'(x) = c\}$.

Proof. Assume that H is a hyperplane. Then $H = x_0 + H_0$ where $X = \text{span}\{H_0 \cup \{x_1\}\}$, x_1 not in H_0. Then for each $x \in X$, $x = \alpha x_1 + h_0$, $h_0 \in H_0$, and this representation is unique. With $x'(x) = \alpha$, it is clear that $H = \{x; x'(x) = x'(x_0)\}$.

Conversely, assume $H = \{x; x'(x) = c\}$ for some scalar c and a nontrivial linear functional x'. Then there is an x_0 such that $x'(x_0) = 1$.

Let L be the null space of x'. Then, if $x'(x) = d$, $x - dx_0 \in L$, and we see that $\{x_0\} \cup L$ spans X. Hence L is a subspace of codimension one and $H = \{x; x'(x) = c\} = cx_0 + L$. This completes the proof.

Thus the linear functional x' plays the role of the "normal" to the hyperplane $x'(x) = c$. If x_0 is a point of the hyperplane, then its equation can always be written $x'(x - x_0) = 0$. The hyperplane divides the space into the two "sides" $x'(x) \geq c$ and $x'(x) \leq c$.

Let X be a linear space which is also a topological space and let Φ be the associated scalar field, either the reals or the complexes with their usual topology. Then X is a *linear topological space* if the mappings

$(x_1, x_2) \rightarrow x_1 + x_2$ of $X \times X \rightarrow X$ and $(\alpha, x) \rightarrow \alpha x$ of $\Phi \times X \rightarrow X$ are continuous.

A *normed linear space* is a linear space X together with a function, called the norm and denoted $\| \cdot \|$, defined on it which "measures the distance to zero" of an element of X and satisfies: (1) $\|x\| \geq 0$ and $\|x\| = 0$ if and only if $x = 0$; (2) $\|x + y\| \leq \|x\| + \|y\|$; and (3) $\|\alpha x\| = |\alpha|\,\|x\|$, where $x \in X$ and $\alpha \in \Phi$. One may note that given a norm, if we define $\rho(x, y) = \|x - y\|$, then ρ is a metric, and hence the norm can be used to define a metric topology. It is easily seen that a normed linear space, understood to have the norm-induced topology, is a linear topological space. If the normed linear space is complete it is called a *Banach Space*.

As an example, we consider the $\mathscr{L}_p$ *spaces*. Two real-valued functions defined on the real interval $[0, T]$ will be called *equivalent* if the set on which they differ has Lebesgue measure zero. Let $1 \leq p < \infty$ be given. Let X be the linear space of equivalence classes of Lebesgue measurable functions f defined on $[0, T]$ for which $\int_0^T |f(\tau)|^p \, d\tau < \infty$. For $f \in X$ we define $\|f\| = \left[\int_0^T |f(\tau)|^p \, d\tau\right]^{1/p}$. With this definition of norm, X becomes a complete normed linear space which is usually denoted by $\mathscr{L}_p[0, T]$.

If X is the space of essentially bounded real-valued functions f on $[0, T]$, we define $\|f\| = \text{ess sup} |f(\tau)|$ and obtain the complete normed linear space $\mathscr{L}_\infty[0, T]$.

If X and Y are normed linear spaces, a linear operator $T : X \rightarrow Y$ is *continuous* if and only if there is an $M > 0$ such that $\|Tx\| \leq M\|x\|$ for all $x \in X$. The set of all continuous linear operators from X to Y, with the usual definitions of addition and scalar multiplication, is itself a linear space. One may define a norm of an element T in this space to be $\|T\| = \sup\{\|Tx\| : \|x\| = 1\}$, and the associated norm induced topology is called the *uniform operator topology* for the space.

Consider, in particular, the case when X is a normed linear space and Y is the scalar field Φ, which is itself a normed linear space. The set of all continuous linear mappings from X to Y is then the set of all continuous linear functionals on X. With the norm defined as above, it is denoted by X' and called the *normed conjugate* or *normed dual* of X.

If X is merely a linear topological space, the linear space of all continuous linear functionals on X is again denoted by X' and is called the *conjugate* or *dual* space of X. We will not associate any specific topology with X' in this case.

It is well known for $1 < p < \infty$ that the normed conjugate space $\mathscr{L}'_p[0, T]$ of $\mathscr{L}_p[0, T]$ is (congruent to) $\mathscr{L}_q[0, T]$ where $1/p + 1/q = 1$. Also $\mathscr{L}'_1[0, T]$ is $\mathscr{L}_\infty[0, T]$, but the converse is *not* true.

5. Convex Sets and the Hahn-Banach Theorem

Let X be a linear space. Note that we proceed first with just the linear structure of X. A set K in X is *convex* if, whenever $x, y \in K$, the " line segment" $\alpha x + (1 - \alpha)y$, $0 \leq \alpha \leq 1$, joining x to y also belongs to K. A point x is called an *internal* point of a set S in X if given any $y \in X$ there is an $\varepsilon > 0$ such that $x + \delta y \in S$ for all real $|\delta| < \varepsilon$. Geometrically, x is an internal point of S if the intersection of S with any " line" through x contains a segment with x as midpoint. A point is called a *bounding point* of S if it is neither an internal point of S nor of its complement.

Let K be a convex set in X which has an internal point. Without loss of generality we may assume the internal point to be the origin. Define a real-valued function ρ on X as follows. Let $I(x) = \{\alpha > 0; (1/\alpha)x \in K\}$ and $\rho(x) = \inf\{I(x)\}$. Then ρ is called a *support function* of K. Geometrically this can be interpreted as follows. For any nonzero point $x \in X$ consider the ray from the origin through x. If $\rho(x) = 0$, the ray is contained in K. If $\rho(x) > 0$, the ray leaves K at the point $y = (1/\rho(x))x$, and y is a bounding point of K. The function ρ satisfies: $0 \leq \rho(x) < \infty$; $\rho(\alpha x) = \alpha \rho(x)$, $\alpha > 0$; $\rho(x + y) \leq \rho(x) + \rho(y)$; if $x \in K$, $\rho(x) \leq 1$; internal points of K have $\rho(x) < 1$; bounding points satisfy $\rho(x) = 1$.

To motivate the Hahn-Banach theorem, and in particular some of its uses in control theory, let K be a closed, bounded, convex set in E^n which does not contain the origin. One may ask: is there a point in K nearest the origin and if so how may we characterize it? Geometrically we can define a *support hyperplane* to be a hyperplane which has a nonempty intersection with K but such that K lies entirely on one side of this plane. Intuitively, and actually, in order that a point $x \in K$ be closest to the origin it must belong to the boundary of K and a support plane to K containing x must have a unit normal, at x, which "points to the origin."

The Hahn-Banach theorem is an analogous result for more general linear spaces. A nontrivial linear functional will take the place of a normal to the hyperplane in the above example. However, the existence of supporting hyperplanes is by no means obvious or even true, in general. If X is a linear topological space, it is possible to have a dense hyperplane in X; i.e., the closure of the hyperplane is X. To avoid this and to obtain something analogous to the finite-dimensional, geometrically motivated model, we will have to consider hyperplanes of the form $\{x \in X; x'(x) = c\}$ where x' is a continuous linear functional on X and c some constant. We will continue for the moment, however, with the nontopological case. For simplicity, the results will be stated and proved for real linear spaces (i.e., the associated field is the reals), although the theorems can be extended to complex linear spaces.

Theorem 5.1 (Algebraic Hahn-Banach Theorem). Let X be a real linear space and ρ a real-valued function defined on X which satisfies:

$$\text{(i)} \qquad \rho(ax) = a\rho(x), \quad a > 0$$

$$\text{(ii)} \quad \rho(x + y) \leqq \rho(x) + \rho(y).$$

Let x'_0 be a real linear functional defined on a subspace L of X such that $x'_0(x) \leqq \rho(x)$ for all $x \in L$. Then x'_0 admits an extension x' to all of X which is linear and satisfies $x'(x) \leqq \rho(x)$ for all $x \in X$.

Proof. We may assume L is a proper subspace of X. We first will show for any $y \notin L$ that x'_0 can be extended to a linear functional x'_1 defined on L_1, the space spanned by L and y, in such a way that $x'_1(x) \leqq \rho(x)$ on L_1.

If $x \in L_1$, then $x = \alpha y + l$ for some real α and some $l \in L$, and this representation is unique. Therefore we must have $x'_1(x) = \alpha x'_1(y) + x'_0(l)$, and this leaves us with the question of whether or not we can assign a value to $x'_1(y)$ which will satisfy $x'_1(x) \leqq \rho(x)$ for all $x \in L_1$. This is equivalent to

$$\alpha x'_1(y) \leqq \rho(\alpha y + l) - x'_0(l)$$

for all real α and all $l \in L$, which in turn is easily seen to be equivalent to

$$-\rho(-y - \beta l) - x_0'(\beta l) \leq x_1'(y) \leq \rho(y + \beta l) - x_0'(\beta l)$$

for all real β and all $l \in L$. Again this is equivalent to

$$m = \sup_{l \in L}(-\rho(-y - l) - x_0'(l)) \leq x_0'(y) \leq \inf_{l \in L}(\rho(y + l) - x_0'(l)) = M.$$

If we knew that $m \leq M$, then by assigning $x_1'(y)$ any value between m and M we would obtain a suitable extension x_1' of x_0' to L_1. Now for any $l_1, l_2 \in L$

$$x_0'(l_1) - x_0'(l_2) = x_0'(l_1 - l_2) \leq \rho(l_1 - l_2) \leq \rho(l_1 + y) + \rho(-l_2 - y).$$

Therefore

$$-\rho(-l_2 - y) - x_0'(l_2) \leq \rho(l_1 + y) - x_0'(l_1)$$

for all $l_1, l_2 \in L$. Hence $m \leq M$ and this shows we can properly extend x_0' to L_1.

We now form a partially ordered system $\mathscr{P}$ of all linear extensions x' of x_0' which satisfy $x'(x) \leq \rho(x)$ on the domain of x'. The partial order relation is defined by $x_1' \leq x_2'$ if x_2' is an extension of x_1'. We have shown, above, that $\mathscr{P}$ is not empty. Also any completely ordered subset has an upper bound, the extension defined on the union of the domains of definitions of the extensions in the totally ordered subset. Applying Zorn's lemma gives a maximal extension of x_0', which must necessarily be defined on all of X. Indeed, if there were a point y not in its domain, our above argument shows that we can extend this functional to include y in such a way that the desired inequality with ρ holds. Therefore this maximal element is the required functional.

Theorem 5.2 Let M and N be convex sets in a real linear space X. Assume that M has at least one internal point and N contains no internal point of M. Then there is a nontrivial linear functional x' such that $x'(x) \leq c$ for $x \in M$ and $x'(x) \geq c$ for $x \in N$. (When x' has this property it is said to *separate* M and N.)

Proof. Assume, without loss of generality, that 0 is an internal point of M. Let $x_0 \in N$ and define

$$K = x_0 + M - N = \{x_0 + m - n : m \in M, n \in N\}.$$

Then K is convex, $M = x_0 + M - x_0 \subset K$, and since 0 is an internal point of M it is an internal point of K.

We next show that x_0 is not an internal point of K. Suppose it were. Then $M - N = K - x_0$ would have 0 as an internal point. For any $y \neq 0$ and some positive α, the point αy would belong to $M - N$; i.e., $\alpha y = m - n$ for some $m \in M$, $n \in N$, or $(\alpha y + n)/(\alpha + 1) = m/(\alpha+1)$. Suppose, in particular, we choose $y \in N$. The left side of the above equality is a point on the line segment joining y to n in N, and hence belongs to N since N is convex. Since 0 is an internal point of M, it readily follows from the convexity of M that $m/(\alpha + 1)$ is an internal point of M. This contradicts the hypothesis that N contains no internal points of M. Therefore x_0 is not an internal point of K.

Now let $\rho(x)$ be the support function of K. Then $\rho(x_0) \geq 1$ and ρ satisfies the hypotheses of Theorem 5.1. To apply this theorem define x_0' on the one-dimensional subspace L spanned by x_0 as follows: $x_0'(ax_0) = a\rho(x_0)$, a real. Then if $a > 0$, $x_0'(ax_0) = \rho(ax_0)$, while if $a \leq 0$, $x_0'(ax_0) \leq 0$, which is less than or equal to $\rho(ax_0)$. Theorem 5.1 now applies and yields an extension x' of x_0' defined on all of X and satisfying $x'(x) \leq \rho(x)$.

For $x \in K$, $x'(x) \leq \rho(x) < 1$ while $x'(x_0) = \rho(x_0) \geq 1$, and x' separates x_0 and K. But points in K have the form $x_0 + m - n$, $m \in M$ and $n \in N$. Hence $x'(x_0 + m - n) \leq 1$, and $x'(x_0) \geq 1$ implies $x'(m - n) \leq 0$ or $x'(m) \leq x'(n)$, $m \in M$, $n \in N$. With $c = \sup\{x'(m); m \in M\}$ this implies x' separates M and N.

We now consider analogous theorems for normed linear spaces. If K is a convex set in a normed linear space X, an interior point of K (i.e., a point with a neighborhood contained in K) is an internal point of K. The converse is not necessarily true.

Theorem 5.3 (Topological Hahn-Banach Theorem). Let x_0' be a continuous linear functional defined on a linear subspace L of a real normed linear space X. Let $\|x_0'\|_L = \sup\{|x_0'(x)|; x \in L, \|x\| = 1\}$ denote the norm of x_0' on L. Then x_0' may be extended to a continuous linear functional x' defined on all of X without increasing its norm.

Proof. Let $\rho(x) = \|x_0'\|_L \|x\|$. Then ρ satisfies the conditions of Theorem 5.3, and, in fact, ρ is a norm on X. Thus there exists an x' defined on all of X, which extends x'_0, such that $x'(x) \leq p(x) = \|x'_0\|_L \|x\|$, $-x'(x) = x'(-x) \leq p(-x) = \|x'_0\|_L \|x\|$ which together imply $|x'(x)| \leq p(x) = \|x'_0\|_L \|x\|$ for all $x \in X$. This shows that x' is continuous and $\|x'\| = \|x'_0\|_L$.

Before deriving a separation theorem analogous to Theorem 5.2, we shall prove two lemmas. These lemmas, and Theorem 5.4, which follows, can be extended to include linear topological spaces. (This is not the case, however, for the corollary to Theorem 5.4.) For our needs, and for simplicity, we confine ourselves to normed linear spaces.

Lemma 5.1 A linear functional x' on a real normed linear space X is continuous if and only if its null space $L = \{x; x'(x) = 0\}$ is closed.

Proof. If x' is continuous its zeros from a closed set. This shows necessity. For sufficiency we may assume $x' \neq 0$ and its null space L is a closed hyperplane. By linearity, it suffices to show continuity at the origin.

Suppose x_0 is such that $x'(x_0) = 1$. Then $M = x_0 + L = \{x; x'(x) = 1\}$ is a closed hyperplane (Lemma 4.1), not containing the origin, on which x' has the value 1.

Since M is closed and does not contain 0, $r = \inf\{\|x\|; x \in M\} > 0$. If $x'(x) \neq 0$, then $(1/x'(x))x \in M$ and hence $|x'(x)| \leq (1/r)\|x\|$. This shows that x' is continuous.

Lemma 5.2 If a linear functional x' on a real normed linear space X separates two sets, one with an interior point, then x' is continuous.

Proof. We first note that a hyperplane is either dense in X or closed. Indeed if L is a hyperplane, $L \subset \bar{L} \subset X$ (the bar denoting closure). Then either $L = \bar{L}$ or $\bar{L} = X$. For if L were not closed $\bar{L}$ contains elements not in L. Since each is a linear space (the closure of a linear subspace is easily shown to be a linear subspace) and L has codimension one, $\bar{L}$ must be X.

Let M be the set with the interior point and suppose $x'(x) \geq c$ for $x \in M$. With a translation, if necessary, we may assume $c > 0$. Then the null space L of x' is disjoint from M. Since M contains an interior point, L cannot be dense in X. Hence being a hyperplane L is closed, and, from Lemma 5.1, x' is continuous.

Theorem 5.4 Let M and N be convex sets in a real normed linear space X. Assume that M has at least one interior point and that N contains no interior point of M. Then there is a nontrivial continuous linear functional x' such that $x'(x) \leq c$ for $x \in M$, $x'(x) \geq c$ for $x \in N$. Furthermore if M is open, $x'(x) < c$ for $x \in M$, $x'(x) \geq c$ for $x \in N$.

Proof. Since an interior point is an internal point, Theorem 5.2 applies to yield a linear functional x' which separates M and N. From Lemma 5.2 this functional must be continuous.

Suppose that M were open and contained a point x_0 such that $x'(x_0) = c$. From the continuity of x' it would follow that the inverse image of some real neighborhood of c would be contained in M, contradicting $x'(x) \leq c$ for all $x \in M$.

Corollary 5.1 If X is a real normed linear space, $x_1, x_2 \in X$, $x_1 \neq x_2$, then there exists a nontrivial continuous linear functional x' such that $x'(x_1) \neq x'(x_2)$. This implies also that if $x'(x) = 0$ for all continuous linear functionals x' on X, then $x = 0$.

The proof follows from the previous theorem by taking an open ball about x_1 which does not contain x_2. This generalizes to linear topological spaces X with the property that for any two distinct points x_1, x_2 in X there is a convex neighborhood of one which does not contain the other.

6. Dual Variational Problems and the Foundations of Moment Problems

Theorem 6.1 Let M be a linear subspace of a real normed linear space X and let d denote the distance from some point x to M. If $x' \in X'$ vanishes on M then $|x'(x)| \leq d\|x'\|$. Furthermore there exists a linear functional $x' \in X'$, vanishing on M, for which equality holds.

Before undertaking a proof let us look at the geometric meaning of this result. Let M^0 denote the continuous linear functionals which vanish on M. Then the theorem states that

$$d = \inf_{m \in M} \|x - m\| = \max\{x'(x); x' \in M^0, \|x'\| = 1\}.$$

In Euclidean space this means geometrically that the length of the projection of x on each unit vector x' which is orthogonal to M is less than or equal to the distance d from x to M. Furthermore there exists a unit vector x' orthogonal to M for which $|x'(x)| = d$.

Proof. Since the result is trivial when $d = 0$, we assume $d > 0$. For $m \in M$ and $x' \in M^0$, $|x'(x)| = |x'(x - m)| \leq \|x'\| \, \|x - m\|$. Hence

$$|x'(x)| \leq \inf_{m \in M} \|x'\| \, \|x - m\| \quad \text{or} \quad |x'(x)| \leq d\|x'\|.$$

We next must construct a linear functional in M^0 for which equality holds. We first define a continuous linear functional x_0' on the span $\{M, x\}$ and then extend it to all of X by Theorem 5.3.

An element in span $\{M, x\}$ has the form $\alpha x - m$, $m \in M$; define $x_0'(\alpha x - m) = \alpha d$. Then if $\alpha = 0$, $x_0'(m) = 0$; i.e., x_0' vanishes on M. Also, since M is a subspace, $0 \in M$ and $x_0'(x) = d$. To show that x_0' is continuous, note that

$$\|x_0'\| = \sup\left\{\frac{|x_0'(\alpha x - m)|}{\|\alpha x - m\|}; \quad m \in M, \quad \alpha x - m \neq 0\right\}$$

$$= \sup_m\left\{\frac{|x_0'(x - m/\alpha)|}{\|x - m/\alpha\|}\right\} = \sup_m \frac{d}{\|x - m\|} = 1$$

by the definition of d. By Theorem 5.3, x_0' has a continuous extension to all of X which satisfies the requirements of the theorem.

The Second Dual Space

If X is a normed linear space, then X' is also a normed linear space, and hence X'' (the space of continuous linear functionals on X') is again a normed linear space with $\|x''\| = \sup\{|x''(x')|; \|x'\| = 1\}$. We define a linear mapping $J: X \to X''$, called the *canonical imbedding*, by the equation $(Jx)(x') = x'(x)$ for all $x' \in X'$, $x \in X$. It is clear that J is well defined; i.e., if $Jx = x_1''$, $Jx = x_2''$ then $(x_1'' - x_2'')(x') = 0$ for all $x' \in X'$, which implies $x_1'' = x_2''$. The normed linear space X is said to be *norm reflexive* if J is onto. We shall show that the mapping J is always one-to-one and norm preserving.

To show that J is one-to-one, suppose $x_1 \neq x_2$. By the corollary to Theorem 5.4 there exists an $x' \in X$, such that $x'(x_1) \neq x'(x_2)$, hence $x'(x_1) = (Jx_1)(x') \neq (Jx_2)(x') = x'(x_2)$. To show J is norm preserving, take $M = \{0\}$ in Theorem 6.1. Then $M^0 = X'$ and we obtain

$$\|x\| = \max\{x'(x); \|x'\| = 1\}. \tag{6.1}$$

Let $Jx = x''$. Then

$$\|x''\| = \sup\{|x''(x')|; \|x'\| = 1\}$$
$$= \sup\{|x'(x)|; \|x'\| = 1\} = \|x\|.$$

The next result is dual to Theorem 6.1.

Theorem 6.2 Let M be a linear subspace of a real normed linear space X and let M^0 be the set of continuous linear functionals in X' which vanish on M. For any $x_0' \in X'$ of distance d from M^0

$$d = \min\{\|x_0' - m'\|; m' \in M^0\} = \sup\{x_0'(x); x \in M, \|x\| = 1\} = \|x_0'\|_M;$$

i.e., the minimum on the left is actually attained by some $m_0' \in M^0$.

Proof. If $m \in M$, Jm vanishes on M^0. Applying Theorem 6.1 to $M^0 \subset X'$ gives

$$|x_0'(m)| = |(Jm)(x_0')| \leq d\|Jm\| = d\|m\| \quad \text{or} \quad \|x_0'\|_M \leq d.$$

To complete the proof, we will construct $m_0' \in M^0$ such that $d \leq \|x_0' - m_0'\| = \|x_0'\|_M$. By Theorem 5.3 there is an $x' \in X'$ which agrees with x_0' on M and with $\|x'\| = \|x_0'\|_M$. Take $m_0' = x_0' - x'$. Then m_0' vanishes on M and

$$\|x_0'\|_M \leq d = \inf\{\|x_0' - m'\|; m' \in M^0\} \leq \|x_0' - m_0'\| = \|x'\| = \|x_0'\|_M.$$

Therefore equality holds for m_0'.

This theorem is the basis for many results in moment problems.

The next theorem is similar to Theorem 6.1 but replaces the subspace M by a convex set K; i.e., it characterizes the distance from an arbitrary point to a convex set. It has many applications, particularly in linear control theory, convex programing, and game theory.

Theorem 6.3 Let K be a convex set in a real normed linear space and let x_0 be a point a positive distance d from K. Then

$$d = \inf_{x \in K} \|x - x_0\| = \inf_{x \in K} \max_{\|x'\| = 1} x'(x - x_0) = \max_{\|x'\| = 1} \inf_{x \in K} x'(x - x_0),$$

(6.2)

the maximum being achieved by some $x' \in X'$.

For purposes of statement and proof, there is no loss of generality in assuming a translation has been made so that $x_0 = 0$. The statement equivalent to (6.2) then becomes

$$d = \inf_{x \in K} \|x\| = \inf_{x \in K} (\max_{\|x'\| = 1} x'(x)) = \max_{\|x'\| = 1} (\inf_{x \in K} x'(x)),$$

(6.3)

where the maximum is attained by some $x'_1 \in X'$ and furthermore $x'_1(x) \geq d$ for all $x \in K$ ($d > 0$).

Proof. We shall prove (6.3). The first equality is a definition, the second merely uses (6.1) to replace $\|x\|$, and the third is the one we must prove.

For each $x' \in X'$, $\|x'\| = 1$, we know $x'(x) \leq \|x\|$. Thus $\inf_{x \in K} x'(x) \leq \inf_{x \in K} \|x\| = d$. We will show that there exists an $x'_1 \in X'$, $\|x'_1\| \leq 1$ with $x'_1(x) \geq d$ for all $x \in K$, which will show that $\max_{\|x'\| = 1}(\inf_{x \in K} x'(x)) = d$ and thus complete the proof. Note that this will imply $\|x'_1\| = 1$.

Let S be an open ball about the origin of radius d. Then $S \cap K = \emptyset$ and by Theorem 5.4 there exists a nontrivial continuous linear functional x'_0 and a constant c such that $x'_0(y) < c$ for $y \in S$, $x'_0(y) \geq c$ for $y \in K$. Since S is a ball about the origin, $c > 0$ and we may take $c = 1$.

Let $x'_1 = dx'_0$. Then $x'_1(y) < d$ for $y \in S$, $x'_1(y) \geq d$ for $y \in K$ and

$$\|x'_1\| = \sup_{\|x\| = 1} |x'_1(x)| = \sup_{\|x\| = 1} |dx'_0(x)| = \sup_{\|x\| = d} |x'_0(x)| \leq 1.$$

Therefore x'_1 is as desired and it achieves the maximum indicated on the right in (6.3).

Corollary 6.1 Let K be a convex set in a real normed linear space X and x_0 be any point in X. Then x_0 belongs to the closure of K (denoted $\bar{K}$) if and only if, for each $\|x'\| = 1$, $x'(x_0) \leq \sup\{x'(x); x \in K\}$.

Proof. If $x_0 \in \bar{K}$ and $\|x'\| = 1$, certainly $x'(x_0) \leq \sup\{x'(x); x \in K\}$. On the other hand if $x_0 \notin \bar{K}$ its distance to $\bar{K}$ is positive and (6.2) implies the existence of an x', $\|x'\| = 1$, such that $0 < d = \inf_{x \in K} x'(x) - x'(x_0)$ or $x'(x_0) > \inf_{x \in K}(-x'(x)) = \sup_{x \in K} x'(x)$.

7. Weak and Weak * Topologies

Let X be a normed linear space and X' its normed dual space; i.e., the space of continuous, linear, scalar-valued functions on X. Elements of X' constitute a set of functions which can be used, as in Section 3, to generate another topology for X, which is the weak topology generated by X'. This will be the weakest topology for X under which the elements of X' are still continuous.

Taking into consideration that a base for a topology may be formed by taking all finite intersections of elements of a subbase, a base for the *weak topology of X* consists of neighborhoods of the form

$$N(x_0, \varepsilon, A') = \{x \in X; |x'(x - x_0)| < \varepsilon, x' \in A'\}$$

where $\varepsilon > 0$ and A' is a finite subset of X'. The weak topology of X is sometimes denoted $\mathcal{T}(X, X')$, the topology of X generated by the elements of X'. From the corollary to Theorem 5.4 it readily follows that given two points $x_1, x_2 \in X$ with $x_1 \neq x_2$, there are disjoint weak neighborhoods of the points. This shows that the weak topology is a Hausdorff topology.

One may easily show that the weak topology of E^n is the same as the usual Euclidean metric topology. However, for an infinite-dimensional Banach space, the weak topology is *not* metrizable. A sequence $\{x_n\}$ in a normed linear space X *converges weakly* to x (converges in the weak topology) if and only if the scalar sequence $\{x'(x_n - x)\}$ converges to zero for each fixed $x' \in X'$. Geometrically this means that the distance (in norm) from x_n to each hyperplane through x tends to zero.

From Corollary 6.1 and the definition of weak neighborhoods one may easily show that a convex set $K \subset X$ is *closed in the norm topology if and only if it is closed in the weak topology*. Indeed, the weak topology is weaker than the norm topology, hence K closed in the weak topology implies K closed in the norm topology. Conversely if $x_0 \notin K$ Corollary 6.1 shows we may find a weak neighborhood of x_0 disjoint from K. Thus the complement of K is open in the weak topology and K is closed.

If X is a normed linear space, X' and X'' are both normed linear spaces. The canonical imbedding J of Section 6 yields a one-to-one correspondence between X and the range of J in X''. Therefore, we can consider elements x of X as continuous linear functionals on X' with $x(x') = (Jx)(x')$. This means that X' has two quite natural weak topologies: that induced by X'' which is the weak topology for X' [denoted $\mathcal{T}(X', X'')$], and that induced by the elements of X. The latter is called the weak $*$ topology and denoted $\mathcal{T}(X', X)$. If X is reflexive (i.e., J is onto) the weak and weak $*$ topologies for X' are the same. If X is not reflexive, the weak $*$ topology of X' is weaker than its weak topology. One may easily show that a normed linear space, with either the weak or weak $*$ topology, is a linear topological space.

Lemma 7.1 Let X' be the normed conjugate space of a real normed linear space X and x_1', x_2' be two distinct points in X'. Then there exists an element $x \in X$ such that $(Jx)(x_1') \neq (Jx)(x_2')$. Essentially, this shows that the weak $*$ topology of X' is a Hausdorff topology.

Proof. Since x_1' and x_2' are distinct, there is an x for which $x_1'(x) \neq x_2'(x)$, from which the result follows.

The weak topology was defined so that the linear functionals which were continuous on X with its norm topology are still continuous when X has its weak topology. This leads to:

Lemma 7.2 Let T be a continuous linear mapping from X, with its norm topology, to E^n. Then T is continuous as a mapping of X, with its weak topology, to E^n. (E^n is Euclidean n space.)
  Let $T = (T_1, \ldots, T_n)$ be a continuous linear mapping from X', with its norm topology, to E^n such that the components T_i of T are representable as elements of X. Then T is continuous as a mapping of X', with the weak $*$ topology, to E^n.

Since the weak topology of an infinite-dimensional Banach space is *not* a metric topology, sequences and compactness versus sequential compactness must be handled with care. In particular, one may have a point x in the weak closure of a set S such that no sequence in S converges weakly to x. Thus a generalized notion of sequence, in particular one in which the index set has larger cardinality than that of the integers, is needed. This has led to the definitions of nets and filters, which however will not be dealt with here. To stress, again, what may happen in an infinite-dimensional Banach space X with its weak topology we point out that it is possible to construct a sequence $\{x_n\}$ such that every weak neighborhood of zero contains a point of $\{x_n\}$ yet $\{x_n\}$ has no subsequence converging to zero.

One may wonder why the normed topology of a normed linear space should be discarded in favor of the weak topology. For our purposes, the main reason is the following. A set S which is not compact in the strong, or norm, topology may be compact in the weak topology. The weaker the topology, the more likely a set will be compact. For instance, with the indiscrete topology for a set X, every subset is compact. It is easily shown that the closed unit ball in an infinite-dimensional normed linear space is *not* compact in the norm topology. On the other hand, a result which is basic to control theory is:

Theorem 7.1 Let X be a real normed linear space. The closed unit ball $S' = \{x' \in X': \|x'\| \leq 1\}$ of X' is compact in the weak * topology $\mathscr{T}(X', X)$.

Proof. Let Φ denote the scalar field. For $x \in X$ let d_x be the closed unit disk $\{\lambda \in \Phi : |\lambda| \leq \|x\|\}$ in Φ. Then d_x is compact. Define $C = \prod_{x \in X} d_x$. By Tychonoff's theorem (Theorem 3.1) C is compact. An element $c \in C$ can be considered as a function on X with value $c(x) \in d_x$; then $|c(x)| \leq \|x\|$, and C can be considered as the set of all such functions.

For $x' \in S'$ we have $|x'(x)| \leq \|x\|$; therefore, we may think of S' as a subset of C. In particular, with $x' \in S'$ we associate the element $c \in C$ such that $c(x) = x'(x)$.

Let C/S' denote the complement of S' in C. We will show that C/S' is open in C and hence S' is closed in C and therefore compact. Since the topology $\mathscr{T}(X', X)$ of S' is just the relative topology of S' induced by the topology of C, S' will have been shown to be compact in the weak * topology $\mathscr{T}(X', X)$.

It therefore remains to show that C/S' is open in C. Now $c_0 \in C/S'$ maps X into E' and is not linear. Therefore either (i) there exist $x_1, x_2 \in X$ such that $c_0(x_1) + c_0(x_2) \neq c_0(x_1 + x_2)$ or (ii) there exists $\alpha \in E'$ and $x \in X$ such that $c_0(\alpha x) \neq \alpha c_0(x)$. In Case (i) there exists an $\varepsilon > 0$ such that $c_0(x_1) + \eta_1 + c_0(x_2) + \eta_2 \neq c_0(x_1 + x_2) + \eta_3$ for all $\eta_i \in (-\varepsilon, \varepsilon)$

and

$$\{c \in C; |c(x_1) - c_0(x_2)| < \varepsilon, |c(x_2) - c_0(x_2)|$$
$$< \varepsilon, |c(x_1 + x_2) - c_0(x_1 + x_2)| < \varepsilon\}$$

is open, contains c_0, and is in C/S'. In Case (ii) there is an $\varepsilon > 0$ such that $c_0(\alpha x) + \eta_1 \neq \alpha c_0(x) + \eta_2$ for all $\eta_i \in (-\varepsilon, \varepsilon)$ and

$$\{c \in C; |c(\alpha x) - c_0(\alpha x)| < \varepsilon, |\alpha c(x) - \alpha c_0(x)| < \varepsilon\}$$

is an open set in C/S' containing c_0. Therefore C/S' is open and this completes the proof.

Corollary 7.1 Let X be a real normed linear space and $Q' \subset X'$ be bounded in the norm topology and closed in the weak $*$ topology of X'. Then Q' is compact in the weak $*$ topology $\mathcal{T}(X', X)$.

Proof. Since Q' is bounded in the norm topology, it is contained in a sufficiently large closed ball of X'. From Theorem 7.1 the closed unit ball of X' is weak $*$ compact; clearly a closed ball of any finite radius is also weak $*$ compact. Thus Q' is a closed subset of a compact set, hence compact.

8. Extreme Points, Exposed Points, and the Liapunov Theorem

Let X be a linear space and K a set in X. A point $x \in K$ is an *extreme point* of K if whenever $x = \alpha k_1 + (1 - \alpha)k_2$, $k_1, k_2 \in K$, $0 < \alpha < 1$, then $k_1 = k_2$. In words, x is an extreme point of K if it cannot be written as a proper convex combination of two distinct elements of K. If K is convex this is equivalent to stating that x is an extreme point of K if x is not the midpoint of any nondegenerate line segment in K. Although the concept of extreme point does not depend upon the topology, we often have to use topological methods to establish their existence.

Now let X be a linear topological space and let K be a set in X. If there is a nontrivial linear functional η' such that $\inf\{\eta'(x - y); x \in K\} = 0$, then the hyperplane through y defined by $\{x \in X; \eta'(x - y) = 0\}$ is called a *support plane* $\pi(\eta)$ of K at y. Since $\eta'(x - y) \geqq 0$ for all $c \in K$, the functional η' can be thought of as an "inner normal" to K at y and K is said "to lie on one side" of this hyperplane. A point $x \in K$ is an *exposed* point of K if K has a closed support hyperplane at x which has only x as its intersection with K. Since the closed support hyperplanes are sets on which a continuous linear functional is constant, the concept of an exposed point is relative to the topology of the space. For X a non-reflexive Banach space, it is possible to have a convex set $K' \subset X'$ such that x' is an exposed point of K' when X' is considered with its weak topology but not an exposed point in X' with its weak $*$ topology.

An exposed point will always be an extreme point, but even in E^2 it is possible to have a convex set with an extreme point which is not an exposed point. Indeed consider a unit circle S^1 in the plane and a point p outside S^1. Draw the tangents from p to S^1, intersecting S^1 at points q and r. Then the line segments pr and pq together with the larger arc qr of S^1 bound a convex set. The points q and r are extreme points of this set which are not exposed.

Lemma 8.1 (Krein–Milman). Let X be a real linear topological space with the property that for any two distinct points x_1 and x_2 of X there is a continuous linear functional x' with $x'(x_1) \neq x'(x_2)$. Then each nonempty compact set K of X has at least one extreme point.

Proof. A nonvoid subset A of K is said to be an *extremal subset* of K if whenever a proper convex combination $\alpha k_1 + (1 - \alpha)k_2$, $0 < \alpha < 1$, of two points of K is in A then both k_1 and k_2 are in A. Clearly K is always an extremal subset of itself and an extremal subset of K which consists of a single point is an extreme point.

Suppose x_1 and x_2 are distinct points of X and x' is a continuous linear functional such that $x'(x_1) \neq x'(x_2)$. Then, in the scalar field, there are disjoint open convex neighborhoods of $x'(x_1)$ and $x'(x_2)$. The inverse images of these neighborhoods, under x', will be disjoint open neighborhoods of x_1 and x_2 in X which shows that X has a Hausdorff topology. In a Hausdorff space, compact sets are closed (Exercise 2.1), and therefore K has at least one closed extremal subset; i.e., K itself.

Let $\mathscr{P}$ be the nonempty family of closed extremal subsets of K, partially ordered by set inclusion. Any totally ordered subset of $\mathscr{P}$ has a minimal element (the nonempty intersection of the elements of the totally ordered subset; that the intersection is nonempty follows from the compactness of K). By Zorn's lemma $\mathscr{P}$ has a minimal element A_0. Suppose A_0 contains two distinct points x_1 and x_2. Let x' be a continuous linear functional such that $x'(x_1) \neq x'(x_2)$ and define $\beta = \inf\{x'(x); x \in A_0\}$. Then $A_1 = \{x \in A_0; x'(x) = \beta\}$ is a closed, nonempty, proper subset of A_0. Since A_0 is an extremal set, if $k_1, k_2 \in K$ and $\alpha k_1 + (1 - \alpha)k_2$ is in A_1 for some $0 < \alpha < 1$, then $k_1, k_2 \in A_0$. But from the definition of A_1, it follows that $k_1, k_2 \in A_1$. Therefore A_1 is a proper, closed, extremal subset of A_0 and this contradicts A_0 being the minimal elements of $\mathscr{P}$. Therefore A_0 contains one point, and this is an extreme point.

In the development of linear optimal control theory Liapunov's theorem on the range of a vector measure [1] played a fundamental role and was first used to establish what is called in control theory the "bang-bang" principle. This important result can be stated, in a more general fashion than we shall do here, as a theorem in abstract measure theory and can be given a direct proof which is, however, both long and complicated. The result which we give here is adequate for linear control theory and can be proved quickly with the tools we have already developed. We will first prove a result which later will provide us with an existence theorem for optimal control and will aid us in obtaining information about the form of optimal control. Next we will prove a "bang-bang" principle and this and the previous result will give us Liapunov's theorem. This reverses the way Liapunov's theorem was first used in control theory, which we will discuss later, and this will show the essential equivalence of Liapunov's theorem and the "bang-bang" principle.

Theorem 8.1 Let I be any subset of the real line having finite Lebesgue measure and let $\Psi = \{u \in \mathscr{L}_\infty(I); 0 \leq u(t) \leq 1\}$. Let y be a (column) vector-valued function with components $y_1, \ldots, y_n$ in $\mathscr{L}_1(I)$. Then the set of points

$$M = \left\{ \int_I y(\tau) u(\tau) \, d\tau; \quad u \in \Psi \right\}$$

is convex and compact.

Proof. Since Ψ is the translation by the function $\frac{1}{2}$ in $\mathscr{L}_\infty(I)$ of the closed ball of radius $\frac{1}{2}$ in $\mathscr{L}_\infty(I)$, it is weak $*$ compact by Theorem 7.1.

Let T be the mapping from $\mathscr{L}_\infty(I)$ to E^n defined by $Tu = \int_I y(\tau)\, u(\tau)\, d\tau$. This is certainly a continuous mapping of $\mathscr{L}_\infty(I)$ relative to its norm topology. Since $\mathscr{L}'_1(I) = \mathscr{L}_\infty(I)$, it follows from the second statement in Lemma 7.2 that T is continuous relative to the weak $*$ topology of $\mathscr{L}_\infty(I)$. T is continuous and linear, Ψ is weak $*$ compact and convex, and therefore its image $T(\Psi) = M$ in E^n is compact and convex. This completes the proof.

For E any subset of the real line the *characteristic function* χ_E is defined to have the value $\chi_E(t) = 1$ for t in E and to be zero elsewhere.

Theorem 8.2 (The Bang-Bang Principle). Let I, Ψ, and M be as in Theorem 8.1. Define $\Psi^0 = \{\chi_E; E$ a measurable subset of $I\}$ and

$$M^0 = \left\{\int_I y(\tau)\, u^0(\tau)\, d\tau; u^0 \in \Psi^0\right\}.$$

Then $M^0 = M$.

Proof. The proof we give is patterned after the proof of the more general theorem given by J. Lindenstrauss [2]. The theorem is *not* true if y is allowed to take values in an infinite-dimensional Banach space and it is not surprising that the proof will be by induction on the dimension n.

Let T be as defined in the proof of Theorem 8.1. It is clear that $M^0 \subset M$. Now $M \subset M^0$ if, for each $a = (a_1, \ldots, a_n) \in M$, $T^{-1}(a) = \{u \in \Psi; Tu = a\}$ contains a characteristic function. Since T is continuous, the inverse image of a closed set is closed. Therefore $T^{-1}(a)$ is a nonempty, closed, convex subset of the weak $*$ compact set Ω, which shows that $T^{-1}(a)$ is weak $*$ compact since the weak $*$ topology is a Hausdorff topology. It follows from Lemma 7.1 that the conditions of Lemma 8.1 are satisfied, and therefore $T^{-1}(a)$ has extreme points. We shall show that an extreme point of $T^{-1}(a)$ is of the form χ_E for some measurable subset E of I.

Let u be an extreme point of $T^{-1}(a)$ and suppose there is an $\varepsilon > 0$ and a subset E_1 of I, having positive measure, such that $\varepsilon \le u(t) \le 1 - \varepsilon$ on E_1. It will be shown that this implies the existence of a nonzero $h \in \mathscr{L}_\infty(I)$ such that $-h + u$ and $h + u$ are both in $T^{-1}(a)$; i.e., that u is the midpoint of a line segment in $T^{-1}(a)$ which contradicts its being an extreme point.

Since the proof for $n = 1$ is equivalent to the induction step, only the induction step will be given. We assume the theorem true for $n - 1$ and will show it to be true for n.

Let $E_2 \subset E_1$ be such that both E_2 and $E_3 = E_1 - E_2$ (the complement of E_2 relative to E_1) have positive measure. (This is possible for a nonatomic measure such as Lebesgue measure.) Applying the induction hypothesis, with I replaced, respectively, by E_2 and E_3, there are measurable sets $F_2 \subset E_2$ and $F_3 \subset E_3$ such that

$$\int_{E_2} y_i(\tau)\, \chi_{F_2}(\tau)\, d\tau = \frac{1}{2} \int_{E_2} y_i(\tau)\, d\tau, \qquad i = 1, \ldots, (n-1).$$

$$\int_{E_3} y_i(\tau)\, \chi_{F_3}(\tau)\, d\tau = \frac{1}{2} \int_{E_3} y_i(\tau)\, d\tau, \qquad i = 1, \ldots, (n-1).$$

Define $h_2 = 2\chi_{F_2} - \chi_{E_2}$ and $h_3 = 2\chi_{F_3} - \chi_{E_3}$. Then

$$\int_{E_1} h_2(\tau)\, y_i(\tau)\, d\tau = 0, \qquad i = 1, \ldots, (n-1), \quad |h_2(\tau)| \leqq 1,$$

and h_2 is not zero on E_2. Also

$$\int_{E_1} h_3(\tau)\, y_i(\tau)\, d\tau = 0, \qquad i = 1, 2, \ldots, (n-1), \quad |h_3(\tau)| \leqq 1,$$

and h_3 is not zero on E_3.

Consider $h(\tau) = \alpha h_2(\tau) + \beta h_3(\tau)$. We desire $|\alpha|, |\beta| < \varepsilon$, $\alpha^2 + \beta^2 > 0$, and α, β such that

$$\int_{E_1} h(\tau)\, y_n(\tau)\, d\tau = \alpha \int_{E_1} h_2(\tau)\, y_n(\tau)\, d\tau + \beta \int_{E_1} h_3(\tau)\, y_n(\tau)\, d\tau$$

$$= 0.$$

Clearly this can be done. With such a choice of α and β, h is not identically zero in E_1; it is zero elsewhere in I, $|h(\tau)| < \varepsilon$, and $\int_I y(\tau)\, h(\tau)\, d\tau = 0$. Therefore $-h + u$ and $u + h$ belong to $T^{-1}(a)$, giving a contradiction to u being an extreme point.

Combining Theorems 8.1 and 8.2 we then have immediately:

Corollary 8.1 (Liapunov's Theorem on the Range of a Vector Measure). The set M^0 is convex and compact.

In a form that we want later on we have, as a corollary of Theorems 8.1 and 8.2,

Corollary 8.2. Let Y be an $n \times r$-matrix-valued function with components y_{ij} in $\mathscr{L}_1[0, t^*]$. Let Ω be the set of r-vector-valued measurable functions u whose components u_j satisfy $|u_j(t)| \leq 1$, $j = 1, \ldots, r$. Let Ω^0 be that subset of Ω for which $|u_j(t)| = 1$, $j = 1, \ldots, 2$. Then $\{\int_0^{t^*} Y(\tau) u(\tau) \, d\tau; u \in \Omega\}$ is symmetric, convex, and compact and

$$\left\{ \int_0^{t^*} Y(\tau) u(\tau) \, d\tau; \quad u \in \Omega \right\} = \left\{ \int_0^{t^*} Y(\tau) u^0(\tau) \, d\tau; \quad u^0 \in \Omega^0 \right\}. \quad (8.1)$$

Proof. Let y^j denote the jth column of Y. Then

$$\int_0^{t^*} Y(\tau) u(\tau) \, d\tau = \sum_{j=1}^{r} \int_0^{t^*} y^j(\tau) u_j(\tau) \, d\tau. \quad (8.2)$$

Define

$$R_j = \left\{ \int_0^{t^*} y^j(\tau) u_j(\tau) \, d\tau; \quad u_j \in \Omega \right\},$$

$$R_j^0 = \left\{ \int_0^{t^*} y^j(\tau) u_j^0(\tau) \, d\tau; \quad u_j^0 \in \Omega^0 \right\},$$

and using the notation of Theorems 8.1 and 8.2,

$$M_j = \left\{ \int_0^{t^*} y^j(\tau) v_j(\tau) \, d\tau; \quad v_j \in \Psi \right\},$$

$$M_j^0 = \left\{ \int_0^{t^*} y^j(\tau) v_j^0(\tau) \, d\tau; \quad v_j^0 \in \Psi^0 \right\}.$$

By Theorems 8.1 and 8.2 we know that M_j is convex and compact and $M_j = M_j^0$. With $u_j(\tau) = 2v_j(\tau) - 1$ we see that Ω and Ω^0 are affine transformations of Ψ and Ψ^0. Therefore R_j and R_j^0 are affine transformations of M_j and M_j^0, and hence R_j is convex and compact and $R_j = R_j^0$. Then (8.1) and the convexity and compactness of $R = \{\int_0^{t^*} Y(\tau) u(\tau) \, d\tau; u \in \Omega\}$ is an easy consequence of (8.2). Since Ω is symmetric, R is symmetric, and this completes the proof.

Another interesting consequence of these results is:

Corollary 8.3 (Richter [3]). Let I be any subset of the real line having finite Lebesgue measure and let G be any function defined on I with values in the set of subsets of E^n. Define $K = \{\int_I s(\tau)\, d\tau;\ s$ measurable, $s(\tau) \in G(\tau)\}$. Then K is convex.

Proof. If there are no measurable functions, or at most one measurable function s on I with values $s(\tau) \in G(\tau)$, the result is trivial.

Assume, therefore, that s^0 and s^1 are measurable on I with values $s^i(\tau) \in G(\tau)$. Let $r_i = \int_I s^i(\tau)\, dt$ and $0 < \alpha < 1$. We will show there is a measurable function s^θ with $s^\theta(\tau) \in G(\tau)$ and $\int_I s^\theta(\tau)\, d\tau = \theta r_0 + (1 - \theta)r_1$.

Consider the $2n$-dimensional vector-valued function $s^2 = (s^0, s^1)$. By Corollary 8.1, $\{\int_I s^2(\tau)\, \chi_E(\tau)\, d\tau:\ E$ is a measurable subset of $I\}$ is convex in E^{2n}. For $E = \varnothing$ and $E = I$, we see that 0 and $(\int_I s^0(\tau)\, d\tau, \int_I s^1(\tau)\, d\tau)$ belong to this set; hence there is an E_θ such that $(\int_{E_\theta} s^0\, d\tau, \int_{E_\theta} s^1\, d\tau) = \theta(\int_I s^0\, d\tau, \int_I s^1\, d\tau)$. Define

$$
s^\theta(\tau) = \begin{cases} s^0(\tau) & \text{for} \quad \tau \in E_\theta \\ s^1(\tau) & \text{for} \quad \tau \in I - E_\theta. \end{cases}
$$

Then

$$
\int_I s^\theta(\tau)\, d\tau = \int_{E_\theta} s^0(\tau)\, d\tau + \int_{I-E_\theta} s^1(\tau)\, d\tau
$$
$$
= \theta r_0 + (1 - \theta)r_1.
$$

This completes the proof.

Theorems 8.1 and 8.2 have been stated for the special case $0 \leq u(t) \leq 1$, thereby simplifying the proofs and statements and readily yielding the important Corollary 8.2 which is fundamental for considering linear control systems with the control u a measurable r-vector-valued function with component values $|u_j(t)| \leq 1$. For simplicity of presentation and notation, this is the type of admissible control function considered throughout most of the monograph. However the possibility of extending future results to include controls which are measurable functions with values in an arbitrary compact set U (which may vary with time) contained in E^r depends on a generalization of Theorems 8.1 and 8.2 and Corollary 8.2, which we now give.

Let I be a subset of the real line having finite Lebesgue measure;

let σ^r be the simplex, in real $(r + 1)$–dimensional space R^{r+1},

$$\sigma^r = \left\{ (\xi_0, \ldots, \xi_r) \in R^{r+1} : 0 \leq \xi_i \leq 1, \quad \sum_0^r \xi_i = 1 \right\}$$

and let $V(\sigma^r)$ be the set of $r + 1$ vertices of σ^r. We will use the notation $\mathscr{L}_\infty^{r+1}(I)$ to mean the topological product of $\mathscr{L}_\infty(I)$ taken with itself $(r + 1)$ times. Then $u \in \mathscr{L}_\infty^{r+1}(I)$ implies that each component $u_i \in \mathscr{L}_\infty(I)$.

Theorem 8.3 Let $Y(t)$ be an $n \times (r + 1)$-matrix-valued function with components in $\mathscr{L}_1(I)$. Then $\{\int_I Y(\tau) u(\tau) \, d\tau : u$ measurable, $u(\tau) \in \sigma^r$ for $\tau \in I\} = \{\int_I Y(\tau) u(\tau) \, d\tau : u$ measurable, $u(\tau) \in V(\sigma^r), \ \tau \in I\}$ and both of these sets are compact and convex

Proof. To simplify notation, let

$$\Psi = \{u \in \mathscr{L}_\infty^{r+1}(I) : u(t) \in \sigma^r, \ t \in I\}$$

$$\Psi^0 = \{u \in \mathscr{L}_\infty^{r+1}(I) : u(t) \in V(\sigma^r), \quad t \in I\}$$

and define

$$T : \mathscr{L}_\infty^{r+1}(I) \to E^n \qquad \text{by} \quad Tu = \int_I Y(\tau) u(\tau) \, d\tau.$$

Clearly Ψ is convex and bounded in the norm topology; hence, by Corollary 7.1, if we can show Ψ is weak $*$ closed it will be weak $*$ compact. Suppose u^0 is a weak $*$ limit of Ψ which does not belong to Ψ. Then there is a set $E \subset I$ of positive measure such that $u^0(t) \notin \sigma^r$ for $t \in E$. One may readily establish the existence of an $\varepsilon > 0$ and $\eta \in E^{r+1}$ such that the inner product $(\eta, \xi) \geq C$ if $\xi \in \sigma^r$ and $(\eta, u^0(t)) < C - \varepsilon$ for t in a subset E_1 of E having positive measure $\mu(E_1)$. Define a function $w(t) = (w_0(t), \ldots, w_r(t))$ in $\mathscr{L}_1^{r+1}(I)$ by

$$w_i(t) = \begin{cases} \eta_i/\mu(E_1) & \text{for} \quad t \in E_1, \\ 0 & \text{for} \quad t \notin E_1. \end{cases}$$

Then w separates u^0 and Ψ, contradicting u^0 being a weak $*$ limit of Ψ. Thus Ψ is closed, convex, and weak $*$ compact. By Lemma 7.2, T is weak $*$ continuous; therefore $T\Psi = \{Tu : u \in \Psi\}$ is a compact, convex subset of E^n.

To complete the proof we must show the equality of $T\Psi$ and $T\Psi^0$. Clearly $T\Psi^0 \subset T\Psi$. If $a \in T\Psi$, $T^{-1}(a) \cap \Psi$ is a weak $*$ compact, convex subset of Ψ and hence, by Lemma 8.1, has an extreme point u. The proof will be complete if we can show u is in Ψ^0.

Suppose $u \notin \Psi^0$. $V(\sigma^r)$ consists of $(r + 1)$ points; enumerate them as $v^0, \ldots, v^r$. Then there is a set $E_1 \subset I$ having positive measure and such that $|u(t) - v^i| > \varepsilon > 0$ for all $t \in E_1$ and $i = 0, \ldots, r$. We will show this implies the existence of a nonzero $h \in \mathscr{L}_\infty^{r+1}(I)$ such that $-h + u$ and $h + u$ are both in $T^{-1}(a) \cap \Psi$; i.e., that u is the midpoint of a line segment in $T^{-1}(a) \cap \Psi$, contradicting its being an extreme point. We will construct h so that $u(t) \pm h(t) \in \sigma^r$ for $t \in E_1$, $h(t) = 0$ for $t \in I - E_1$, and $\int_{E_1} Y(\tau) h(\tau) \, d\tau = 0$. This will show both $-h + u$ and $h + u$ are in $T^{-1}(a) \cap \Psi$ as required.

Let $E_2 \subset E_1$ be such that both E_2 and $E_3 = E_1 - E_2$ (the complement of E_2 relative to E_1) have positive measure. This is possible for a nonatomic measure such as Lebesgue measure. We will give an induction argument for the construction of h, the induction being on the row dimension n of the matrix $Y(t)$. For the remainder of this proof, $y^i(t)$ will denote the ith *row* of the matrix $Y(t)$ and $(y^i(t), h(t))$ the inner product of $y^i(t)$ and $h(t)$ in E^{r+1}.

For $n = 1$ order the elements $v^0, \ldots, v^r$ of $V(\sigma^r)$ and define $F_j = \{t \in E_2 : |u(t) - v^j| \text{ equals the distance from } u(t) \text{ to } V(\sigma^r) \text{ with } j \text{ the smallest index for which this equality holds}\}$. Clearly $F_j \cap F_i = \varnothing$ if $i \neq j$, $\bigcup_{j=0}^r F_j = E_2$ and each F_j is measurable. Define h^2 on E_2 by defining its restriction to F_j as $(1/2r)(u(t) - v^j)$, $j = 0, \ldots, r$. Then $h^2 \neq 0$ on E_2 and $u(t) \pm h^2(t) \in \sigma^r$. Extend h^2 to be zero on $I - E_2$. We define a function h^3 on E_3 similarly. Let $h(t) = \alpha h^2(t) + \beta h^3(t)$. Clearly we may choose $|\alpha|, |\beta| \leq 1$, $\alpha^2 + \beta^2 > 0$ such that

$$\int_{E_1} (y^1(t), h(t)) \, dt = \alpha \int_{E_2} (y^1(t), h^2(t)) \, dt + \beta \int_{E_3} (y^1(t)$$
$$h^3(t)) \, dt = 0$$

and for such values α, β, h is as desired.

Now use the induction hypothesis for $n - 1$ with the set E_1 replaced by E_2. Thus there exists a nonzero measurable function h^2 defined on E_2, with $u(t) \pm h^2(t) \in \sigma^r$, such that $\int_{E_2} (y^i(\tau), h^2(\tau)) \, d\tau = 0$ for $i = 1, 2, \ldots, n - 1$ and h^2 is zero on $I - E_2$. Similarly apply the induction hypothesis with E_1 replaced by E_3 to obtain a nonzero function h^3 defined on E_3 with $u(t) \pm h^3(t) \in \sigma^r$, $\int_{E_3} (y^i(\tau), h^3(\tau)) \, d\tau = 0$,

$i = 1, \ldots, n - 1$ and h^3 is zero on $I - E_3$. Consider $h(t) = \alpha h^2(t) + \beta h^3(t)$. Again choose $|\alpha|, |\beta| \leq 1$, $0 < \alpha^2 + \beta^2$ and such that

$$0 = \int_{E_1} (y''(\tau), h(\tau)) \, d\tau = \alpha \int_{E_2} (y''(\tau), h^2(\tau)) \, d\tau + \beta \int_{E_3} (y''(\tau), h^3(\tau)) \, d\tau.$$

This completes the induction step for the construction of h, and thereby completes the proof.

Let F be a function defined on the real interval I with values $F(t)$ nonempty compact subsets of a fixed compact set in E^n. We shall assume F is continuous in the Hausdorff topology (see Exercise 3.1) but this can be weakened to F measurable (see the remark following the proof of the next theorem).
    Define

$$\int_I F(\tau) \, d\tau = \left\{ \int_I f(\tau) \, d\tau : f \text{ measurable}, f(\tau) \in F(\tau), \tau \in I \right\}$$

and let co F denote the function with values co $F(t)$ the convex hull of $F(t)$. The desired generalization of Corollary 8.2 is:

Theorem 8.4 (Aumann [4]). $\int_I F(\tau) \, d\tau = \int_I \text{co } F(\tau) \, d\tau$ and both are convex, compact, subsets of E^n.

Proof. Convexity follows from Corollary 8.3.

    We next show the equality. Certainly $\int_I F(\tau) \, d\tau \subset \int_I \text{co } F(\tau) \, d\tau$. Suppose $y \in \int_I \text{co } F(\tau) \, d\tau$. Then $y = \int_I f(\tau) \, d\tau$ for some measurable f with values $f(\tau) \in \text{co } F(\tau)$. By Caratheodory's theorem (Eggelston [5], p. 34) for each $\tau \in I$ the point $f(\tau) \in \text{co } F(\tau)$ may be written as a convex combination of $n + 1$ points of $F(\tau)$; i.e.,

$$f(\tau) = \sum_{i=0}^{n} \xi_i(\tau) f^i(\tau), \qquad f^i(\tau) \in F(\tau) \tag{8.3}$$

$$0 \leq \xi_i(\tau) \leq 1, \qquad \sum_{i=0}^{n} \xi_i(\tau) = 1.$$

We let $\xi(\tau)$ denote the vector function $(\xi_0(\tau), \ldots, \xi_n(\tau)) \in \sigma^n$.
    The proof of the theorem will be completed under the assumption that the functions ξ_i, f^i can be chosen as measurable. This will then be proven in Lemma 8.2 which follows. Let the vectors $f^i(t)$ be the columns

of an $n \times (n + 1)$ matrix $Y(t)$. By theorem 8.3 there exists a measurable vector function $\xi^*(t) = (\xi_0^*(t), \dots, \xi_n^*(t))$ taking values in the vertices of the simplex σ^n such that

$$\int_I f(t)\, dt = \int_I Y(t)\, \xi(t)\, dt = \int_I Y(t)\, \xi^*(t)\, dt.$$

Now $\xi_i^*(t) = \{^0_1$ for all t and i and $\sum_{i=0}^n \xi_i^*(t) = 1$. Let $I_i = \{t \in I: \xi_i^*(t) = 1\}$. Then each I_i is measurable, $\bigcup_{i=0}^n I_i = I$, $I_i \cap I_j = \varnothing$ if $i \neq j$. Define $f^*(t) = f^i(t)$ for $t \in I_i$. Then f^* is measurable, $f^*(t) \in F(t)$ and $\int_I f^*(t)\, dt = \int_I f(t)\, dt$, showing $\int_I F(t)\, dt = \int_I \text{co } F(t)\, dt$.

To show compactness we need only show $\int_I \text{co } F(t)\, dt$ is compact. Let $\Lambda = \{f \in \mathscr{L}_2^n(I): f(t) \in \text{co } F(t), t \in I\}$. Then, since each $F(t)$ is closed and bounded, Λ is a closed, bounded, convex subset of $\mathscr{L}_2^n(I)$. From Section 7, Λ is closed in the weak topology. But $\mathscr{L}_2^n(I)$ is reflexive so the weak and weak $*$ topologies are the same. Corollary 7.1 then shows that Λ is weakly compact. Define $\mathscr{I} : \mathscr{L}_2^n(I) \to E^n$ by $\mathscr{I}(f) = \int_I f(\tau)\, d\tau$. Then $\mathscr{I}$ is weakly continuous; hence $\mathscr{I}(\Lambda)$ is compact, i.e., $\int_I \text{co } F(t)\, dt$ is compact. This completes the proof.

REMARK. Define a compact set valued function F to be *measurable* if, for any closed set $D \subset E^n$, $\{t \in I: F(t) \cap D \neq \varnothing\}$ is Lebesgue measurable. Plis' [6] has proven the following generalization of Luzin's theorem.

Let F be a measurable set valued function defined on I with values nonempty compact subsets of E^n. Then given any $\varepsilon > 0$ there exists a closed set $B \subset I$ with measure differing from that of I by less than ε, on which F is continuous in the Hausdorff topology.

We next will state and prove the representation lemma needed to complete the proof of Theorem 8.4. Note that it is this use of the lemma in completing the proof of Theorem 8.4 that requires continuity (or measurability) of F. The lemma will be stated so that the proof is self-contained for the case F continuous and complete except for the proof of Plis' theorem of the preceding remark for the case F measurable.

Lemma 8.2 (Filippov [7]). Let $g(v) = g(v_1, \dots, v_m)$ be a continuous n-vector-valued function of the m real variables $v_1, \dots, v_m$. Let $H(t)$ be a continuous (measurable) function defined on the real interval I with values nonempty compact subsets of a fixed compact subset of E^m. Define

$$R(t) = \{g(v): v \in H(t)\}.$$

Then if $r(t)$ is a measurable function with values $r(t) \in R(t)$ there exists a measurable function $v(t)$ with values in $H(t)$ such that $r(t) = g(v(t))$ almost everywhere in I.

Proof. For given $r \in R(t)$ we select from these $v \in H(t)$ which satisfy $g(v) = r$ the one with smallest first component. If there is more than one, we take that with the smallest second component, and so on. The smallest values exist since g is continuous, $H(t)$ is compact, hence $g^{-1}(r) \cap H(t)$ is compact. We shall show by induction that the functions $v_1(t), \ldots, v_m(t)$ so chosen are measurable. Suppose $v_1(t), \ldots, v_{s-1}(t)$ are measurable. (If $s = 1$ there is nothing to assume.) We must show that $v_s(t)$ is measurable. By Luzin's theorem, for any $\varepsilon > 0$ there exists a closed set $E \subset I$ of measure greater than $\mu(I) - \varepsilon$ such that $r(t), v_1(t), \ldots,$ $v_{s-1}(t)$ are continuous on E. (If we deal with the case H measurable we use Plis' generalization of Luzin's theorem as stated in the preceding remark to include H continuous on E.) We will show that, for any number a, $\{t \in E: v_s(t) \leq a\}$ is closed.

Suppose not. Then there exists a sequence $\{t_n\}$ in E such that

$$t_n \to t' \in E, \qquad v_s(t_n) \leq v_s(t') - \varepsilon_1, \quad \varepsilon_1 > 0. \tag{8.4}$$

Since $|v_i(t)|$ is bounded by a constant for all i and t, a subsequence of the t_n can be chosen (we assume it is the original sequence) so that $v_i(t_n) \to v_i'$ for $i = 1, 2, \ldots, m$. Since $v(t_n) \in H(t_n)$ and H is continuous on E and $H(t')$ is closed, $(v_1', \ldots, v_m') = v' \in H(t')$. From (8.4) and the continuity of the functions v_i, $i = 1, 2, \ldots, s - 1$ on E, it follows that

$$v_i' = v_i(t') \qquad \text{for} \quad i = 1, 2, \ldots, s - 1,$$
$$v_s' \leq v_s(t') - \varepsilon_1. \tag{8.5}$$

Taking a limit in the identity $g(v_1(t_n), \ldots, v_m(t_n)) = r(t_n)$ and using the continuity of g we obtain $g(v_1(t'), \ldots, v_{s-1}(t'), v_s', \ldots, v_m') = r(t')$. From this and (8.5) we see $v_s(t')$ is *not* the smallest value of v_s satisfying the equation $g(v_1(t'), \ldots, v_{s-1}(t'), v_s, \ldots, v_m) = r(t')$. This contradicts the definition of $v_s(t)$; thus $\{t \in E: v_s(t) \leq a\}$ must be closed. This shows v_s is measurable on E. Since $E \subset I$ and the measure $\mu(E)$ differs from

$\mu(I)$ by at most ε with $\varepsilon > 0$ and arbitrary, v_s is measurable on I and the induction step is complete, as is the proof.

To use Lemma 8.2 in the proof of Theorem 8.4 choose

$$g(\xi, \beta^0, \ldots, \beta^n) = \sum_{i=0}^{n} \xi_i \beta^i \quad \text{and} \quad H(t) = \sigma^{n+1} \times F(t) \times \cdots \times F(t)$$

with $F(t)$ appearing $n + 1$ times in the product. Then, in (8.3), f is a measurable function with values $f(t)$ in $g(\sigma^{n+1}, F(t), \ldots, F(t))$. By Lemma 8.2 we may take the functions $\xi_i(t)$, $f^i(t)$ satisfying (8.3) to be measurable.

9. Finite-Dimensional Vector Space

Although we assume throughout a knowledge of linear algebra and finite dimensional vector (linear) spaces, we discuss them here briefly in order to introduce notations we shall adopt throughout. Let V_n be an n dimensional vector space over the reals, and let $\xi^1, \ldots, \xi^n$ be a basis of V_n. Then each ξ in V_n is uniquely represented by $\xi = x_1\xi^1 + x_2\xi^2 + \cdots + x_n\xi^n$. This then establishes an isomorphism between V_n and n dimensional real space R^n with the one to one mapping of V_n onto R^n defined by

$$\xi \sim x = \begin{pmatrix} x_1 \\ \vdots \\ x_n \end{pmatrix}.$$

We assume a knowledge of matrix operations, and denote the vectors in R^n by column vectors ($n \times 1$ matrices). If A is an $n \times k$ matrix, A' denotes its transpose. Thus the scalar or inner product of two vectors y and x in R^n is

$$y'x = y_1 x_1 + \cdots + y_n x_n$$

and

$$|x|^2 = x'x = x_1^2 + \cdots + x_n^2.$$

This defines a norm on R^n making it a normed linear space often denoted (as we have previously done) by E^n. We shall, however, use the notations R^n and E^n interchangeably.

In R^n we write $|x|$ for $\|x\|$. This makes the basis $\xi^1, \ldots, \xi^n$ an orthonormal basis. If $\eta = y_1\xi^1 + \cdots + y_n\xi^n$ and $\xi = x_1\xi^1 + \cdots + x_n\xi^n$, this induces an inner product $(\eta, \xi) = y'x$ in V_n. With this inner product V_n is a normed linear space that is congruent (isometrically isomorphic) to R^n. If η' is a linear function on V_n $(\eta' \in V_n')$, then

$$\eta'(\xi) = y'x,$$

where $\xi = x_1\xi^1 + \cdots + x_n\xi^n$ and $y_i = \eta'(\xi^i)$. Each linear functional can be represented as an inner product and V_n is reflexive.

In general, if A is an $n \times k$ matrix, we define

$$\|A\| = \max\{\|Ax\|\,; |x| = 1, x \in R^k\}.$$

Thus, $\|A\|^2$ is the maximum eigenvalue of $A'A$. Note also that $\|ABx\| \leq \|A\| \cdot \|Bx\| \leq \|A\| \cdot \|B\| \cdot |x|$, and therefore

$$\|AB\| \leq \|A\| \cdot \|B\|.$$

In Section 8 above we defined support planes and exposed points for general linear topological spaces. We now wish to confine ourselves to n dimensional Euclidean space R^n. Here the linear functionals are given by the inner product $(\eta, x) = \eta'x$, where $\eta \in R^n$. If

$$x = \begin{pmatrix} x_1 \\ \vdots \\ x_n \end{pmatrix} \quad \text{and} \quad \eta = \begin{pmatrix} \eta_1 \\ \vdots \\ \eta_n \end{pmatrix},$$

then $\eta' = (\eta_1, \ldots, \eta_2)$ is the transpose of η and $\eta'x = \eta_1 x_1 + \cdots + \eta_n x_n$. Thus all linear functionals are continuous and all hyperplanes defined by $\eta'x = $ const are closed. For finite dimensional vector spaces we then have the following result:

A hyperplane in R^n is said to *separate* two sets if they lie on opposite sides of the hyperplane. Since the closure of a convex set is closed we shall confine ourselves to closed convex sets.

Theorem 9.1 Let K be a closed convex set in R^n and let w be a point of R^n not in K. Then there exists a support plane of K at the point w^* of K closest to w that separates K and w, and is normal to $w - w^*$.

Proof. Since $d = d(w, K) = \inf_{y \in K} |y - w| > 0$, there exists a sequence $y^n \in K$ such that $|w - y^n| \to d$ as $n \to \infty$. Since the sequence y^n is bounded, it has a limit point w^* in K and $d = |w - w^*|$. By Theorem 6.3

$$d = |w - w^*| = \inf_{y \in K} \eta'(w - y) \qquad \text{for some} \quad |\eta| = 1.$$

Hence

$$|w - w^*| = \eta'(w - w^*) \leqq |w - w^*|,$$
$$\eta'(w - w^*) = |w - w^*|,$$

and therefore

$$\eta = \frac{w - w^*}{|w - w^*|}.$$

For $y \in K$,

$$\eta'(y - w^*) = \eta'(w - w^*) - \eta'(w - y) \leqq 0;$$

i.e., the hyperplane π normal to η at w^* is a support plane to K. Since the line segment from w to a point y of K intersects π in exactly one point, w^* is unique.

Corollary 9.1 Let K be a closed convex set of R^n and let $w(t)$ be a continuously differentiable function on $[0, t^*]$ to R^n. If $w(t) \notin K$ for $0 \leqq t < t^*$ and $w(t^*) \in K$, then there is a support plane $\pi(\eta)$ to K at $w(t^*)$ with outward normal η and such that $\eta'\dot{w}(t^*) \leqq 0$. ($\dot{w} = dw/dt$.)

Proof. For each $w(t)$, $0 \leqq t < t^*$, let $w^*(t)$ be the point of K closest $w(t)$. By Theorem 9.1 there is a support plane $\pi(\eta(t))$ to K normal to

$$\eta(t) = \frac{w(t) - w^*(t)}{|w(t) - w^*(t)|}$$

which separates $w(t)$ and K for each $0 \leqq t < t^*$. Since the unit sphere in R^n is compact and $w^*(t) \in K$ are bounded, there exists a sequence t_n such that $t_n \to t^*$, $w^*(t) \to q \in K$, and $\eta(t) \to \eta$ ($|\eta| = 1$) as $n \to \infty$. It is easy to see that $q = w(t^*)$ and $\pi(\eta)$ is a support plane of K at $w(t^*)$. Since

$$0 < \eta'(t_n)(w(t_n) - w^*(t_n)) = \eta'(t_n)[w(t_n) - w(t^*)] + \eta'(t_n)(w(t^*) - w^*(t_n))$$

and

$$\eta'(t_n)(w(t^*) - w^*(t_n)) < 0,$$

it follows that

$$\eta'(t_n)\left(\frac{w(t^*) - w(t_n)}{t^* - t_n}\right) < 0.$$

The proof is completed by letting $n \to \infty$.

Corollary 9.2 Through each point of the boundary of a closed convex set in R^n there is a support plane.

Proof. This is a simple special case of Corollary 9.1.

The above corollary is not true for infinite dimensional linear topological spaces even if K is assumed to be compact and the boundary point is assumed to be an extreme point.

For later use we define now the concept of "strict convexity." A closed convex set K is said to be *strictly convex* if it contains more than one point and each of its boundary points is an exposed point; that is, each support plane has exactly one point in common with K. It is not difficult to see that a strictly convex set in R^n has a nonempty interior (Exercise 9.1).

EXERCISE 9.1. Show that each strictly convex set in R^n has a nonempty interior.

EXERCISE 9.2. Let M be a closed convex set in R^n and N a compact convex set in R^n. If M and N do not intersect, show that M and N have parallel support planes each of which separate M and N.

EXERCISE 9.3. Let $M(t)$ and $N(t)$ be set functions on $[0, t^*]$ to the set of nonempty compact convex sets of R^n which are continuous relative to the Hausdorff metric for compact sets in R^n. If $M(t)$ and $N(t)$ do not intersect for $0 \le t < t^*$ and intersect for $t = t^*$, show that $M(t^*)$ and $N(t^*)$ have a common support plane that separates $M(t^*)$ and $N(t^*)$.

EXERCISE 9.4. Let N be a closed convex set of R^n and let $M(t)$ be as in Exercise 9.3. If N and $M(t)$ do not intersect for $0 \le t < t^*$ but N and $M(t^*)$ intersect, show that $M(t^*)$ and N have a common support plane that separate $M(t^*)$ and N.

10. Linear Differential Equations

For the most part the differential equation of interest to us will be of the form ($\dot{x} = dx/dt$)

$$\dot{x} = A(t)\,x + f(t), \tag{10.1}$$

where A is an $n \times n$ matrix-valued function and f is an n vector-valued function whose components (a_{ij} and f_i) are Lebesgue summable on finite intervals of $[0, \infty)$. A function x on $[0, \infty)$ to R^n will be said to be a *solution* of (9.1) *on* $[0, \infty)$ if x is absolutely continuous on $[0, \infty)$ and satisfies almost everywhere on $[0, \infty)$

$$\dot{x}(t) = A(t)\,x(t) + f(t).$$

Assume for the moment that $f = 0$ and that there does exist a solution $\varphi(t) = x(t; t_0, x^0)$ on $[0, \infty)$ of

$$\dot{x} = A(t)\,x \tag{10.2}$$

satisfying $\varphi(t_0) = x(t_0, t_0, x^0) = x^0$ $(t_0 \geq 0)$. Then with $V(x) = x'x = |x|^2$

$$\frac{d}{dt} V(\varphi(t)) = 2\varphi'(t)A(t)\varphi(t)$$

and

$$-2\|A(t)\|\,|\varphi(t)|^2 \leq \frac{d}{dt} V(\varphi(t)) \leq 2\|A(t)\|\,|\varphi(t)|^2.$$

Hence

$$-2\|A(t)\|V(\varphi(t)) \leq \frac{d}{dt} V(\varphi(t)) \leq 2\|A(t)\|V(\varphi(t)),$$

which implies

$$\frac{d}{dt}\left[\exp\left[2\int_{t_0}^{t} \|A(\tau)\|\,d\tau \right] V(\varphi(t)) \right] \geq 0$$

and

$$\frac{d}{dt}\left[\exp\left[-2\int_{t_0}^{t} \|A(\tau)\|\,d\tau \right] V(\varphi(t)) \right] \leq 0.$$

Together these two inequalities imply

$$\exp\left[-2\left|\int_{t_0}^{t} \|A(\tau)\| \, dt\right|\right] V(x_0) \leq V(\varphi(t)) \leq \exp\left[2\left|\int_{t_0}^{t} \|A(\tau)\| \, d\tau\right|\right] V(x^0)$$

$$(10.3)$$

or

$$\exp\left[-2\left|\int_{t_0}^{t} \|A(\tau)\| \, d\tau\right|\right] |x_0| \leq |x(t, t_0, x^0)| \leq \exp\left[\left|\int_{t_0}^{t} \|A(\tau)\| \, d\tau\right|\right] |x^0|$$

for all $t, t_0 \geq 0$. It then follows immediately from (10.3) that $x(t, t_0, 0)$ $\equiv 0$. The zero function is the unique solution on $[0, \infty)$ of (10.2) satisfying $x(t_0) = 0$.

Assume now that $x(t, t_0, x^0)$ is a solution of (10.1) on $[0, \infty)$ satisfying $x(t^0, t_0, x^0) = x^0$. Since the difference of two solutions of (10.1) is a solution of (10.2), the solution $x(t, t_0, x^0)$, if it exists, is unique.

We will next show that a solution $X(t, t_0)$, $t_0 \geq 0$, of the matrix differential equation

$$\dot{X} = A(t) \, X, \tag{10.4}$$

satisfying $X(t_0, t_0) = I$, exists on $[0, \infty)$. $X(t, t_0)$ is called the *principal matrix solution* of (10.4) at t_0. In fact, we will show that

$$X(t, t_0) = I + \int_{t_0}^{t} A(t_1) \, dt_1 + \int_{t_0}^{t} A(t_2) \int_{t_0}^{t_2} A(t_1) \, dt_1 \, dt_2$$

$$+ \cdots + \int_{t_0}^{t} A(t_n) \int_{t_0}^{t_n} A(t_{n-1}) \cdots A(t_2)$$

$$\times \int_{t_0}^{t_2} A(t_1) \, dt_1 \, dt_2 \ldots dt_n + \cdots.$$

This can be written in a more manageable form. Let M be the set of continuous $n \times n$ matrix valued functions Φ defined on $[0, \infty)$ and define the transformation T of M into itself by

$$T(\Phi)(t) = I + \int_{t_0}^{t} A(\tau) \, \Phi(\tau) \, d\tau.$$

Then the above formula can be written

$$X(t, t_0) = \lim_{n \to \infty} T^n(I)(t).$$

It is not difficult to see that

$$\|T^n(I)(t)\| \leq 1 + \left| \int_{t_0}^t \|A(\tau)\| \, d\tau \right| + \cdots + \frac{1}{n!} \left| \int_{t_0}^t \|A(\tau)\| \, d\tau \right|^n$$

$$\leq \exp\left[\left| \int_{t_0}^t \|A(\tau)\| \, d\tau \right| \right].$$

Therefore $\lim_{n \to \infty} T^n(I)(t) = F(t)$ exists and is continuous on $[0, \infty)$. For Lebesgue integrals it follows easily that

$$T(F(t)) = I + \int_{t_0}^t A(\tau) \lim_{n \to \infty} T^n(I)(\tau) \, d\tau$$

$$= \lim_{n \to \infty} \left(I + \int_{t_0}^t A(\tau) T^n(I)(\tau) \, d\tau \right)$$

$$= \lim_{n \to \infty} T^{n+1}(I)(t) = F(t).$$

Hence

$$F(t) = I + \int_{t_0}^t A(\tau) \, F(\tau) \, d\tau.$$

Therefore $F(t)$ is absolutely continuous and is a solution of (10.4) on $[0, \infty)$ satisfying $F(t_0) = I$. This establishes the existence of the solution we want and $F(t) = X(t, t_0)$.

We then obtain immediately by uniqueness

$$X(t, t_1) X(t_1, t_0) = X(t, t_0) \tag{10.5}$$

for all nonnegative t, t_1, and t_0, since both sides of the equality satisfy (10.4) and the same initial condition at $t = t_1$. With $t = t_0$ in (10.5) we see that $X(t, t_0)$ is nonsingular for all $t \geq 0$ and

$$X(t_0, t_1) = X^{-1}(t_0, t_1).$$

Now it can be either derived or simply verified that *the solution* $x(t, t_0, x^0)$ *of* (10.1) *satisfying* $x(t_0, t_0, x^0) = x^0$ *is*

$$x(t, t_0, x^0) = X(t, t_0)x^0 + \int_{t_0}^t X(t, \tau) \, f(\tau) \, d\tau \tag{10.6}$$

for all nonnegative t and t_0 and all $x^0 \in R^n$. If, in particular, we take $t_0 = 0$ and define $X(t) = X(t, 0)$ then $X(t, t_0) = X(t) X^{-1}(t_0)$, and we obtain

$$x(t, 0, x^0) = X(t)x^0 + X(t) \int_0^t X^{-1}(\tau) \, f(\tau) \, d\tau. \qquad (10.7)$$

When A is a constant matrix we will write

$$\dot{x} = Ax + f(t). \qquad (18.8)$$

Since A is a constant matrix, $X(t, t_0)$ will depend only on $t - t_0$, and again by uniqueness we will have $X(t, t_0) = X(t - t_0, 0) = X(t - t_0)$ and $X(t) X(t_0) = X(t + t_0)$ for all t and t_0. Thus for constant matrices we use $X(t)$ to define the matrix exponential and adopt the notation $X(t) = e^{At}$. It is the solution of $\dot{X} = AX$ satisfying $X(0) = I$. With this notation the solution $x(t, x^0)$ of (10.8) satisfying $x(0, x^0) = x^0$ is

$$x(t, x^0) = e^{At}x^0 + e^{At} \int_0^t e^{-A\tau} f(\tau) \, d\tau \qquad (10.9)$$

for all t and all $x^0 \in R^n$.

The case that will interest us most is

$$\dot{x} = A(t) \, x + B(t) \, u(t), \qquad (10.10)$$

where A and B are $n \times n$- and $n \times r$-matrix valued functions whose components are Lebesgue summable on finite intervals of $[0, \infty)$ and u is an r-vector-valued function whose components are measurable and bounded on finite intervals of $[0, \infty)$. Then $f(t) = B(t) \, u(t)$ has summable components on finite intervals of $[0, \infty)$ and

$$x(t, x^0, u) = X(t)x^0 + X(t) \int_0^t X^{-1}(\tau) \, B(\tau) \, u(\tau) \, d\tau \qquad (10\ 11)$$

is the solution of (10.10) satisfying $x(0, x^0, u) = x^0$ for all $t \geq 0$.

PART II

LINEAR
TIME OPTIMAL CONTROL

11. The General Linear Time Optimal Problem

We consider a control system described by the vector differential equation

$$\dot{x}(t) = A(t)\, x(t) + B(t)\, u(t) \qquad \left(\dot{x}(t) = \frac{d}{dt} x(t)\right) \tag{11.1}$$

with fixed initial data $x(0) = x^0$. The vector

$$x = \begin{pmatrix} x_1 \\ \vdots \\ x_n \end{pmatrix}$$

will always be n dimensional, A and B are $n \times n$- and $n \times r$-matrix-valued functions, respectively, with components summable over finite real intervals, and

$$u = \begin{pmatrix} u_1 \\ \vdots \\ u_r \end{pmatrix}$$

is a measurable vector-valued function with values $u(t)$ constrained to lie in a compact set U of R^r. Let $x(t; u)$ denote the absolutely continuous solution of (11.1) satisfying $x(0) = x^0$. The existence and uniqueness of this solution was discussed in Section 10. The problem is to determine a control u^*, subject to its constraints, in such a way that the solution $x(t; u^*)$ of (11.1) reaches a continuously moving target $z(t)$ in R^n in minimum time $t^* \geq 0$. Such a control u will be termed *time optimal*, or, as we shall say throughout, simply *optimal*. Since the generalization to continuously moving compact sets is not difficult, we restrict ourselves to $z(t)$ a continuously moving point; that is, $z(t)$ defines a continuous curve in the state space R^n. A rendezvous with an orbiting satellite in minimum time presents a problem of this type. Another example is the problem of stabilizing the growth of population in minimum time.

43

This time optimal problem admits a natural geometric interpretation which motivates a method of solution. Define

$$\mathscr{A}(t) = \{x(t; u); \quad u \text{ measurable}, u(\tau) \in U \text{ for } \tau \in [0, t]\}. \quad (11.2)$$

The set $\mathscr{A}(t)$ is called the *attainable set* at time t and consists of all possible values that solutions of (11.1) can assume using all admissible controls. Obviously, hitting the target z at time t is equivalent to $z(t) \in \mathscr{A}(t)$. For example, if U consists of a single point $u^0 \in E^n$, (11.1) has a unique solution $x(t; u^0)$ and $\mathscr{A}(t) = \{x(t; u^0)\}$. In this case, and even more generally, it is easy to see that $\mathscr{A}(t)$ and $z(t)$ may never have points in common.

The existence of an optimal control depends on the following. Is there some value of $t \geq 0$ for which $z(t) \in \mathscr{A}(t)$—a question of "controllability"—and if so, letting $t^* = \inf\{t; z(t) \in \mathscr{A}(t)\}$ is there an admissible control u^* such that $x(t^*; u^*) = z(t^*)$? For the linear system considered, we shall see that the second question is equivalent to the question of whether or not $\mathscr{A}(t^*)$ is closed.

Along with the attainable set $\mathscr{A}(t)$ we shall consider a related set $\mathscr{R}(t)$. Let $X(t)$ be the principal matrix solution (see Section 10) of the homogeneous system $\dot{x}(t) = A(t)x(t)$ [$X(0) = I$, the identity matrix]. Then for an admissible control u (that is, a measurable control with values in U) the solution of (11.1) is given by

$$x(t; u) = X(t)x^0 + X(t) \int_0^t X^{-1}(\tau) B(\tau) u(\tau) d\tau.$$

Define

$$Y(\tau) = X^{-1}(\tau) B(\tau), \qquad w(t) = X^{-1}(t) z(t) - x^0. \quad (11.3)$$

An equivalent optimal control problem is then to find an admissible control u for which $w(t) = \int_0^t Y(\tau) u(\tau) d\tau$ for a minimum value of $t \geq 0$. If we let

$$\mathscr{R}(t) = \{y(t; u); \quad u \text{ measurable}, u(\tau) \in U\}, \quad (11.4)$$

where $y(t; u) = \int_0^t Y(\tau) u(\tau) d\tau$, then

$$\mathscr{A}(t) = X(t)[x^0 + \mathscr{R}(t)] = \{X(t)x^0 + X(t)y; y \in \mathscr{R}(t)\} \quad (11.5)$$

and $z(t) \in \mathscr{A}(t)$ is equivalent to $w(t) \in \mathscr{R}(t)$. Many properties of $\mathscr{R}(t)$ can be immediately translated to similar properties of $\mathscr{A}(t)$ since $\mathscr{A}(t)$

is a translation of $\mathscr{R}(t)$ followed by a linear transformation $X(t)$. This set $\mathscr{R}(t)$ is called the *reachable set* at time t.

The reachable set $\mathscr{R}(t)$ gives a simpler description than does $\mathscr{A}(t)$ of the effect of the control on the system. Another and useful way of looking at this is that under the change of coordinates defined by $x = X(t)y$ the system equivalent to (11.1) is

$$\dot{y} = Y(t)\,u(t). \tag{11.6}$$

Then $y(t; u)$ is the solution of (11.6) satisfying $y(0; u) = 0$ and the objective is now to hit the moving target $w(t)$ in minimum time. Thus u^* is optimal if and only if $w(t^*) \in \mathscr{R}(t^*)$ and $w(t) \notin \mathscr{R}(t)$ for $t < t^*$; t^* is the minimum time.

In order to avoid certain complications it will be convenient to take U to be the unit cube C^r in R^r. Here $C^r = \{u \in R^r; |u_j| \le 1, j = 1, 2, \ldots, r\}$. The *admissible controls* u are then those whose components u_j, $j = 1, 2, \ldots, r$, are measurable on finite intervals with $-1 \le u_j(t) \le 1$ for all $t \ge 0$. Actually what we do here can be extended to U any compact set (even this can be weakened) in R^r. However the results of Section 14 become more difficult to prove and the notation throughout becomes more cumbersome. These generalizations can be accomplished with the aid of Theorem 8.4.

12. General Properties of the Reachable Set and the Bang-Bang Principle

Since we are now restricting ourselves to values of the control function in the unit cube C^r of R^r, the set of admissible controls on $[0, t]$ is given by

$$\Omega[0, t] = \{u; \quad u \text{ measurable on } [0, t], u(\tau) \in C^r, 0 \le \tau \le t\}. \tag{12.1}$$

The reachable set $\mathscr{R}(t)$ is then

$$\mathscr{R}(t) = \left\{ \int_0^t Y(\tau)\,u(\tau)\,d\tau; \quad u \in \Omega[0, t] \right\}.$$

By assumption the components of the matrix B are in $\mathcal{L}_1[0, t]$, the space of Lebesgue summable functions on $[0, t]$, and X^{-1} is an absolutely continuous matrix function on $[0, t]$. Hence the components of $Y = X^{-1}B$ are in $\mathcal{L}_1[0, t]$. Now $\mathcal{R}(t)$ is obviously symmetric for each $t > 0$, since $u \in \Omega$ implies $-u \in \Omega$, and hence we have by Corollary 8.2:

Lemma 12.1   The reachable set $\mathcal{R}(t)$ is symmetric, convex, and compact for all $t \geq 0$.

The second part of Corollary 8.2 contains what is called in control theory the "bang-bang" principle. The set of *bang-bang* controls on $[0, t]$ is

$$\Omega^0[0, t] = \{u; \quad u \text{ measurable}, |u_j(\tau)| = 1, j = 1, \ldots, r, \tau \in [0, t]\}.$$

These are the controls which at all times utilize all the controls available. Then

$$\mathcal{R}^0(t) = \left\{ \int_0^t Y(\tau)\, u^0(\tau)\, d\tau, \quad u^0 \in \Omega^0[0, t] \right\}$$

is the set of points reachable by bang-bang control. By Corollary 8.2 we have:

Theorem 12.1   (The Bang-Bang Principle).

$$\mathcal{R}(t) = \mathcal{R}^0(t) \qquad \text{for each} \quad t \geq 0.$$

This says that any point that can be reached by admissible control in time t can also be reached by bang-bang control in the same time. It had been an intuitive assumption for some time that if the control for a system is operating from a limited source of power and if it is desired to have the system change from one state to another in minimum time, then it is necessary at all times to utilize all the power available; that is, to use bang-bang control. The intuitive feeling is that, if full power is not being used, the use of the additional power available can always speed up the process. In his paper [8] in 1952 Bushaw accepted this hypothesis (and for his problem this was correct) but in this strong form the hypothesis is not always a valid one. There are cases—and we will see simple examples of this later—where there can be more power available than can be used effectively and optimal control is not necessarily always bang-bang. However, the bang-bang principle does say that *if there is an optimal control, then there is always a bang-bang control that is optimal.* Hence if optimal control is unique it is bang-bang.

This bang-bang principle was first proved in [9] using Liapunov's theorem on the range of a vector measure (Corollary 8.1). In Section 8 Liapunov's theorem was shown to be a consequence of the bang-bang principle, and hence the two are equivalent.

There are several other properties of the reachable set that are of importance which we would like to establish now. For the first of these it is convenient to make the set of all nonempty compact subsets of R^n into a metric space (see Section 3, Exercise 3.1) by defining the distance $\rho(A, B)$ between two such subsets A and B to be the smallest real number d so that A is contained in a d neighborhood of B and B in a d neighborhood of A. We then have:

Lemma 12.2 $\mathcal{R}(t)$ is a continuous function on $[0, \infty)$ to the metric space of compact subsets of R^n.

Proof. For each $t_0 \geqq 0$ and $t \geqq 0$

$$|y(t; u) - y(t_0; u)| = \left| \int_{t_0}^t Y(\tau)\, u(\tau)\, d\tau \right| \leqq \left| \int_{t_0}^t \|Y(\tau)\|\, d\tau \right|.$$

It then follows, from the definition of the metric ρ, that

$$\rho(R(t), R(t_0)) \leqq \left| \int_{t_0}^t \|Y(\tau)\|\, d\tau \right|.$$

The conclusion of the lemma follows since $\int_{t_0}^t \|Y(\tau)\|\, d\tau$ is absolutely continuous.

The following is also a result we will need later:

Lemma 12.3   If y is in the interior of $\mathcal{R}(t^*)$ for some $t^* > 0$, then y is an interior point of $\mathcal{R}(t)$ for some $0 < t < t^*$.

Proof. Let N be a neighborhood of y of radius ε inside $\mathcal{R}(t^*)$. Suppose for each $0 < t < t^*$ that y is not an interior point of $\mathcal{R}(t)$. Then by Theorem 9.1 and Corollary 9.1 there is for each $0 < t < t^*$ a hyperplane π_t through y such that $\mathcal{R}(t)$ lies on one side of π_t. Because of the neighborhood N of y that is inside $\mathcal{R}(t^*)$ there is then a point q of $\mathcal{R}(t^*)$ whose distance from $\mathscr{R}(t)$ is at least ε for each $0 < t < t^*$. This contradicts the continuity of $\mathscr{R}(t)$ and completes the proof.

In the proof of the above lemma we made use of the fact that $\mathscr{R}(t)$ is closed, convex, and continuous. It is instructive to note that convexity is essential. Consider the set $\mathscr{R}(t)$ shown in Fig. 12.1, where the angular slice closes continuously and at time t^* has closed along the dotted line and $\mathscr{R}(t^*)$ is a disk. Then at time t^* the point y is in the interior of $\mathscr{R}(t^*)$ but at any time $t < t^*$ the point y is an exterior point of $\mathscr{R}(t)$.

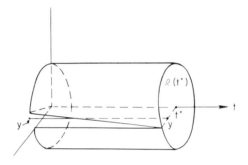

FIG. 12.1.

13. General Theorems on Optimal Control

On the basis of what has gone before we are now in a position to obtain a thorem on the existence of optimal control and a necessary condition for a control to be optimal. The geometric ideas behind the proofs can easily be illustrated for dimension 2. Suppose that the reachable set $\mathscr{R}(t)$ and the moving target $w(t)$ are as shown in Fig. 13.1. The target cannot be reached in time t_1 [Fig. 13.1a] but by time t_2 it is possible to hit the target, $w(t_2) \in \mathscr{R}(t_2)$ [Fig. 13.1b]. The set $\mathscr{R}(t)$ is growing continuously, $w(t)$ is moving continuously, and one then expects that at some time t^* between t_1 and t_2 the situation will be as shown in Fig. 13.1c. This will be the first time $w(t)$ hits $\mathscr{R}(t)$; that is,

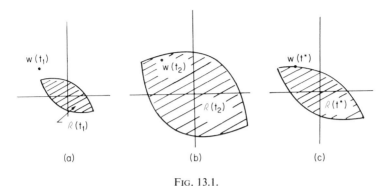

Fig. 13.1.

$w(t^*) = y(t^*; u^*)$. The time t^* will be the minimum time, and u^* will be an optimal control. The point $w(t^*)$ will be on the boundary of $\mathcal{R}(t^*)$, and, since $\mathcal{R}(t^*)$ is convex and closed, there will be a support plane $\pi(\eta)$ at $w(t^*)$. This we will now show is the general picture of what happens, and it will give us an existence theorem and a necessary condition for optimal control. The existence theorem will state that if it is possible to hit the moving target using an admissible control, then there is an admissible control that is optimal. At the moment we have no information about when it is possible to hit the moving target and this is a question of controllability which we will return to later (Section 19). The necessary condition for optimal control gives information on the form of optimal control and this is a special instance of Pontryagin's maximum principle. As we shall see later, this necessary condition is not always sufficient and the information it gives on the form of opitmal control may not be complete. It may, in fact, happen that it gives no information at all.

We have defined admissible controls u relative to an interval $[0, t]$. We will say that a control u defined on $[0, \infty)$ is *admissible* if it is admissible on each finite interval $[0, t)$, $t \geqq 0$; that is, $|u_j(\tau)| \leqq 1$ for each $j = 1, \ldots, r$ and $\tau \geqq 0$ and u is measurable on each finite $[0, t]$, $t \geqq 0$. Let Ω denote the set of all admissible controls. We have that Ω is convex and note also that it has the following property: if u^1 and u^2 are in Ω and E is any measurable subset of $[0, \infty)$ then the control u defined by $u(t) = u^1(t)$ on E and $u(t) = u^2(t)$, elsewhere, is also admissible ($u \in \Omega$).

We then obtain the following existence theorem as a consequence of the fact that $w(t)$ is continuous and $\mathcal{R}(t)$ is continuous and closed:

Theorem 13.1   (Existence of an Optimal Control).   If there is a control $u \in \Omega$ and a $t_1 \geq 0$ for which $x(t_1; u) = z(t_1)$, then there is an optimal control.

Proof. The assumption of the theorem is equivalent to $w(t_1) \in \mathcal{R}(t_1)$. Let $t^* = \inf\{t : w(t) \in \mathcal{R}(t)\}$. Now $0 \leq t^* \leq t_1$ and there is a nonincreasing sequence of times t_n converging to t^* and a sequence of controls $u^n \in \Omega$ with $w(t_n) = y(t_n, u^n) \in \mathcal{R}(t_n)$. Also

$$|w(t^*) - y(t^*, u^n)| \leq |w(t^*) - w(t_n)| + |y(t_n, u^n) - y(t^*, u^n)|$$

$$\leq |w(t^*) - w(t_n)| + \int_{t^*}^{t_n} \|Y(\tau)\| \, d\tau.$$

By the continuity of $w(t)$ and the integrability of $\|Y(t)\|$ it follows that $y(t^*, u^n) \to w(t^*)$ as $n \to \infty$. Since $y(t^*, u^n) \in \mathcal{R}(t^*)$ for each n and $\mathcal{R}(t^*)$ is closed, $w(t^*) \in \mathcal{R}(t^*)$. Hence $w(t^*) = y(t^*, u^*)$ for some $u^* \in \Omega$ and, by the definition of t^*, u^* is optimal.

Given two vectors a, b in R^k we denote the inner product by (a, b) or simply by $a'b$. In keeping with matrix notation a and b are column vectors and a', the transpose of a, is a row vector. We shall also use the notation

$$a = \text{sgn } b \tag{13.1}$$

to mean $a_j = \text{sgn } b_j$, $j = 1, \ldots, k$, where $\text{sgn } b_j = 1$ if $b_j > 0$, $\text{sgn } b_j = -1$ if $b_j < 0$, and when $b_j = 0$ $\text{sgn } b_j$ is undefined. Thus Eq. (13.1) is to be thought of as "a is of the form $\text{sgn } b$"—a satisfies (13.1) wherever $\text{sgn } b_j$ is defined.

Consider, for instance, in the y coordinates the trajectory $y(t; u)$ defined by

$$y(t; u) = \int_0^t Y(\tau) u(\tau) \, d\tau.$$

Then $y(t, u)$ is a solution of

$$\dot{y} = Y(t) u(t). \tag{13.2}$$

Let a nonzero n-vector η define a direction in R^n. Suppose that what we want to do is find an admissible control u that maximizes the rate of change of $y(t; u)$ in the direction η; that is, we want to maximize

$$\eta'\dot{y} = \eta' Y(t)u(t).$$

Since $\eta' Y(t) u(t) = \sum_{j=1}^{r} [\eta' Y(t)]_j u_j(t)$, we see that if u^* is of the form

$$u^*(t) = \text{sgn}[\eta' Y(t)], \quad \eta \neq 0, \tag{13.3}$$

then $\eta' Y(t) u^*(t) = \sum_{j=1}^{r} |[\eta' Y(t)]_j|$. Hence for all $u \in \Omega$

$$\eta' Y(t) u(t) \leq \eta' Y(t) u^*(t) \qquad \text{for all} \quad t \geq 0 \tag{13.4}$$

and

$$\eta' y(t; u) \leq \eta' y(t; u^*) \qquad \text{for all} \quad t \geq 0. \tag{13.5}$$

To dwell on this for a minute, Eq. (13.3) means for each $j = 1, \ldots, r$ that $u_j^*(t) = \text{sgn}[\eta' Y(t)]_j$ when $[\eta' Y(t)]_j \neq 0$. For instance, if $[\eta' Y(r)_j]$ $\neq 0$ almost everywhere, $j = 1, \ldots, r$, then almost everywhere $|u_j^*(t)| = 1$, $j = 1, \ldots, r$, and we say that u^* is *determined* by (13.3). When $|u_j^*(t)| = 1$ almost everywhere for $j = 1, \ldots, r$ we say that the control u^* is *bang-bang*.

Thus a control u^* maximizes $\eta'y(t; u)$ over all admissible controls if and only if u^* is the form (13.3). Therefore for any fixed $t^* > 0$ and any u^* of the form (13.3) the point $q^* = y(t^*; u^*)$ is on the boundary of $\mathscr{R}(t^*)$. Moreover, $\eta'(p - q^*) \leq 0$ for all $p \in \mathscr{R}(t^*)$ and the hyperplane $\pi(\eta)$ through q^* normal to η is a support plane to $\mathscr{R}(t^*)$ at q^* (η is an outward normal to this support plane). Note also that, if u^1 is any other control of the form (13.3) then $y(t^*; u^1)$ lies on this hyperplane $\pi(\eta)$. Conversely, if q^* is on the boundary of $\mathscr{R}(t^*)$, then by Lemma 12.1 and Corollary 9.2 there is support plane $\pi(\eta)$ of $\mathscr{R}(t^*)$ through q^*, and we may take η, which is a nonzero vector, to be an outward normal. Hence we have proved the following:

Lemma 13.1   A point $q^* = y(t^*; u^*)$ is a boundary point of $\mathscr{R}(t^*)$ with η an outward normal to a support plane of $\mathscr{R}(t^*)$ through q^* if and only if u^* is of the form $u^*(t) = \text{sgn}[\eta' Y(t)]$ on $[0, t^*]$ for some $\eta \neq 0$.

From Lemmas 12.3 and 13.1 we obtain immediately:

Theorem 13.2 (A Necessary Condition for Optimal Control). If u^* is an optimal control with t^* the minimum time, then u^*, is of the form $u^*(t) = \text{sgn}[\eta' Y(t)]$ on $[0, t^*]$ for some nonzero vector η.

Proof. Since $t^* = 0$ is trivial, we assume $t^* > 0$. We want to show that $w(t^*) = y(t^*; u^*)$ must be on the boundary of $\mathcal{R}(t^*)$, for then Lemma 13.1 will tell us that u^* is of the form (13.3) on $[0, t^*]$. Assume that $w(t^*)$ is an interior point of $\mathcal{R}(t^*)$. Then by Lemma 12.3 $w(t^*)$ is an interior point of $\mathcal{R}(t_1)$ for some $0 < t_1 < t^*$. Let N be a neighborhood of $w(t^*)$ inside $\mathcal{R}(t_1)$. Then, since $\mathcal{R}(t_1) \subset \mathcal{R}(t)$ for all $t > t_1$, N is contained in $\mathcal{R}(t)$ for all $t > t_1$. The continuity of $w(t)$ then implies that $w(t_2) \in \mathcal{R}(t_2)$ for some $t_2 < t^*$. This contradicts the definition of t^* and $w(t^*)$ is a boundary point of $\mathcal{R}(t^*)$. As pointed at the beginning, this completes the proof.

Note that this theorem and Lemma 13.1 now tell us [and this is essentially (13.5)] that if u^* is an optimal control—and therefore for some $\eta \neq 0$ is of the form $u^*(t) = \text{sgn}[\eta' \ Y(t)]$ on $[0, t^*]$—then the hyperplane $\pi(t, \eta)$ through $y(t; u^*)$ is a support plane to $\mathcal{R}(t)$ for each $t \in [0, t^*]$. In order to show in a moment that this is Pontryagin's maximum principle for the linear time optimal problem, we restate this result relative to the attainable set $\mathcal{A}(t)$ and obtain:

Corollary 13.1 If u^* is an optimal control with t^* the minimum time, then $x(t; u^*)$ is on the boundary of $\mathcal{A}(t)$ for each $t \in [0, t^*]$ and $\psi(t) = \eta' \ X^{-1}(t)$ is an outward normal of a support plane of $\mathcal{A}(t)$ at $x(t; u^*)$ for some $\eta \neq 0$ and each $t \in [0, t^*]$.

EXAMPLE 13.1. Consider the control of the undamped harmonic oscillator

$$\ddot{x} + x = u, \quad |u| \leq 1.$$

An equivalent system of first-order equations is

$$\dot{x} = y$$
$$\dot{y} = -x + u.$$

Hence here

$$A = \begin{pmatrix} 0 & 1 \\ -1 & 0 \end{pmatrix}, \qquad B = \begin{pmatrix} 0 \\ 1 \end{pmatrix},$$

$$X(t) = e^{At} = \begin{pmatrix} \cos t & \sin t \\ -\sin t & \cos t \end{pmatrix}, \qquad Y(t) = e^{-At}B = \begin{pmatrix} -\sin t \\ \cos t \end{pmatrix},$$

and

$$\eta'\, Y(t) = -\eta_1 \sin t + \eta_2 \cos t, \quad \eta_1^2 + \eta_1^2 \neq 0.$$

We can now conclude that if for a given target an optimal control u^* exists, then it is of the form

$$u^*(t) = \operatorname{sgn}(\sin(t + \delta))$$

for some $-\pi \leq \delta \leq \pi$ [since $-\eta_1 \sin t + \eta_2 \cos t = a \sin(t + \delta)$ with $a > 0$]. Therefore, if there is an optimal control, it will be unique, bang-bang ($|u(t)| = 1$ almost everywhere), and its changes of sign occur π units of time apart.

EXAMPLE 13.2. Here we will consider a simple singular case where the necessary condition on optimal control gives no information. For the system

$$\dot{x}_1 = x_1 + u$$
$$\dot{x}_2 = x_2 + u, \quad |u| \leq 1,$$

we see first of all that the control is quite limited. At the point p in Fig. 13.2 the possible directions for the flow lie between the vectors a

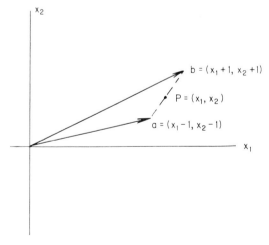

FIG. 13.2.

and b. It is not possible, for instance, to go from p to the origin. It is easier to see the effect of control, by going to the y coordinates,

$$y = e^{-At}x = \begin{pmatrix} e^{-t} & 0 \\ 0 & e^{-t} \end{pmatrix}\begin{pmatrix} x_1 \\ x_2 \end{pmatrix}$$

$$Y(t) = e^{-At}\begin{pmatrix} 1 \\ 1 \end{pmatrix} = \begin{pmatrix} 1 \\ 1 \end{pmatrix}e^{-t}$$

$$\dot{y}_1 = e^{-t}u$$

$$\dot{y}_2 = e^{-t}u.$$

The reachable set (Fig. 13.3) lies on the line $y_1 = y_2$ between the points $(-1, -1)$ and $(1, 1)$.

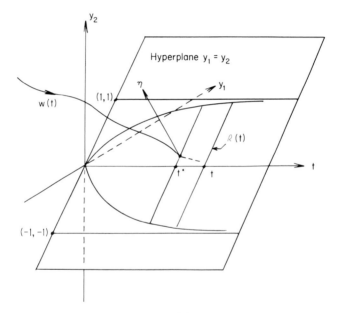

Fig. 13.3.

Here $\eta'Y(t) = (\eta_1 + \eta_2)e^{-t}$ and, when $\eta' = (-1, 1)$, $\eta'Y(t) \equiv 0$. Thus, for instance, if hitting $w(t)$ is as illustrated in Fig. 13.3, the necessary condition gives no information, although it is easy to see what an optimal control is in this case. One could pick $u = 1$ until the point $w(t^*)$ is reached and then turn the control off. Clearly there are an infinity of optimal controls.

EXERCISE 13.1. Give in detail the proof of Corollary 13.1.

EXERCISE 13.2. What can be said about the form of optimal control for:

(a) $\ddot{x} = u,$

(b) $\ddot{x} + 2b\dot{x} + x = u,$

(c) $\dot{x} = y + u_1,$
$\dot{y} = -x - 2by - u_1 + u_2,$

(d) $\dot{x}_1 = u_1 + u_2,$
$\dot{x}_2 = u_1 - u_2,$

(e) $\dot{x}_1 = b_1(t)\, u(t),$
$\dot{x}_2 = b_2(t)\, u(t);$

$$b_1(t) = \begin{cases} 1, & 2n \leq t \leq 2n+1,\ n = 0, 1, \ldots, \\ 0, & \text{otherwise,} \end{cases} \qquad b_2(t) = 1 - b_1(t).$$

EXERCISE 13.3. Consider the system (11.1) and assume x^0 and $t_1 > 0$ are such that $\mathscr{A}(t_1)$ does not contain the origin. Use Theorem 6.3 of Part I to show that: if u^* is an admissible control which is optimal in the sense that $x(t_1, u^*)$ has minimal distance to the origin, then $u^*(t) = \text{sgn}[\eta\, Y(t)]$ on $[0, t_1]$ for some unit vector η.

By means of Corollary 13.1 we can see the relation between this necessary condition and Pontryagin's maximum principle [10]. Following Pontryagin we introduce the Hamiltonian $H(\psi, x, t, u) = \psi(A(t)x + B(t)u)$. Then consider

$$\dot{x} = \frac{\partial H}{\partial \psi} = A(t)x + B(t)u \qquad (13.6)$$

$$\dot{\psi} = \frac{\partial H}{\partial x} = -\psi\, A(t). \qquad (13.7)$$

Equation (13.6) corresponds to (11.1) and $\psi(t) = \eta' X^{-1}(t)$ is the general solution of (13.7). Define

$$M(\psi, x, t) = \max\{H(\psi, x, t, u);\, u \in C^r\}.$$

Pontryagin's maximum principle states that, if u^* is an optimal control, then for some nontrivial solution of (13.7)

$$H(\psi(t), x(t; u^*), t, u^*(t)) = M(\psi(t), x(t; u^*), t)$$

almost everywhere. Here

$$M(\psi, x, t) = \psi(t) \, A(t) \, x + \max_{u \in C^r} \psi \, B(t) \, u$$

$$= \psi(t) \, A(t) \, x + \psi \, B(t) \, u^*(t),$$

where $u^*(t) = \text{sgn}[\psi B(t)] = \text{sgn}[\eta' X^{-1}(t) B(t)] = \text{sgn}[\eta' Y(t)]$. Hence this maximum condition for the linear time optimal problem is equivalent to Theorem 13.2.

EXERCISE 13.4. If A and B are constant matrices, show that $M(\psi(t), x(t; u^*), t) = c$ almost everywhere.

It is interesting to note what this necessary condition means geometrically. At each point of $x(t; u^*)$ the vector $\psi(t)$ is an outward normal to the attainable set $\mathcal{A}(t)$ at $x(t; u^*)$. The quantity $H(\psi(t), x(t; u), t, u(t))$ is proportional to the component of $\dot{x}(t, u)$ in the direction of this normal. At a given time t the choice of the control determines the direction of the flow $\dot{x}(t; u)$ at a point in the state space and *optimal control has the property that it selects a direction for the flow which maximizes its component in the direction of an outward normal to the attainable set at the point.* This is closely related to Bellman's equations of dynamic programing and also to the use of Liapunov functions to design control systems.

With regard to this necessary condition for optimal control it should be pointed out that it states *only* that optimal control is of the form (13.3) for *some* nonzero vector η. However, we do know that at a point of the y space the vector η is an outward normal to the reachable set, and it is this type of structural information about the form of optimal control that makes computational procedures possible. Actually this is enough to enable us to obtain control laws for some simple problems but even for these problems it is helpful to know more about the uniqueness of control, controllability, and to know when this necessary condition is also sufficient.

14. Questions of Uniqueness and Properties of the Boundary of the Reachable Set

Consider the simple control system

$$\dot{x}_1 = u_1,$$
$$\dot{x}_2 = u_2, \qquad |u_1| \leq 1, \quad |u_2| \leq 1.$$

Here

$$B = Y(t) = \begin{pmatrix} 1 & 0 \\ 0 & 1 \end{pmatrix}, \qquad y(t;u) = \int_0^t u(\tau)\, d\tau,$$

and it is not difficult to see that $\mathscr{R}(t^*)$ is a square (Fig. 14.1) with sides of length $2t^*$.

Let the objective be to reach the origin in minimum time ($z(t) \equiv 0$ and $w(t) \equiv -x^0$). Then y on the boundary of $\mathscr{R}(t^*)$ means for this example that it is possible to go from $-y$ to the origin in time t^* and t^*

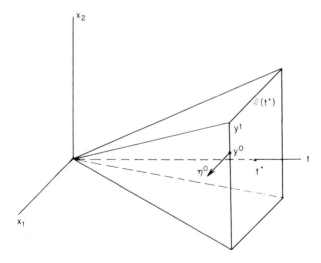

FIG 14.1.

is the minimum time. If y^0 is as shown in Fig. 14.1, then optimal control is certainly not unique. There are an infinite number of optimal controls and optimal trajectories to y even though there is a unique support plane at y^0 with normal

$$\eta^0 = \begin{pmatrix} 1 \\ 0 \end{pmatrix}.$$

In this case

$$\eta^{0\prime} Y(t) = (1, 0),$$

and the necessary condition for optimal control tells us only that $u_1^* = 1$ but gives no information about u_2. At the vertex y^1 of Fig. 14.1, optimal control is unique even though the support plane is not. Taking any outward normal η to $\mathscr{R}(t^*)$ at y^1 with $\eta_1 > 0$, $\eta_2 > 0$, we see that $\eta' Y(t) = (\eta_1, \eta_2)$, and now the necessary condition for optimal control implies $u_1^* = 1$ and $u_2^* = 1$ and determines the control uniquely.

What can happen when B is not a constant matrix is somewhat more complex. For instance, for the system

$$\dot{x}_1 = b_1(t) \, u_1$$
$$\dot{x}_2 = b_2(t) \, u_2,$$

the reachable set $\mathscr{R}(t)$ is a rectangle. The trajectory to a vertex will still be unique but since $b_1(t)$ and $b_2(t)$ can vanish over an interval the control to reach a vertex may not be unique. When $b_1(t) = 0$, the control u_1 has no effect and the choice of u_1 is immaterial. These questions of uniqueness of controls and trajectories are intimately related, and this is what we now want to investigate.

The fundamental control system is, as before,

$$\dot{x} = A(t) \, x + B(t) \, u, \tag{14.1}$$

and all of our discussion will be relative to the reachable set $\mathscr{R}(t)$ and trajectories

$$y(t; u) = \int_0^t Y(\tau) \, u(\tau) \, d\tau.$$

Keep in mind that the attainable set $\mathscr{A}(t)$ is a translation and a linear transformation of $\mathscr{R}(t)$, and you will see that all the results in this section and in Section 16 are true with $\mathscr{R}(t)$ replaced by $\mathscr{A}(t)$. We say that a point q of R^n is *reached in time* t^* if $q \in \mathcal{R}(t^*)$; that is, if for some admissible control u, $q^* = y(t^*; u)$. Now we can consider uniqueness of reaching q in time t^* in different ways. The function $y(\cdot\;; u)$ we call the *trajectory to q in time* t^*; i.e., two *trajectories* $y(\cdot\;; u^1)$ and $y(\cdot\;; u^2)$ are said to be *equal*, if $y(t; u^1) = y(t; u^2)$ for all $t \in [0, t^*]$. Then *uniqueness of the trajectory to q in time* t^* means that $q = y(t^*; u^1) = y(t^*; u^2)$ implies $y(t; u^1) = y(t; u^2)$ for all $t \in [0, t^*]$.

The next concept of uniqueness is associated with "essential equality" of control, which we will now explain. Since

$$y(t; u) = \int_0^t Y(\tau)\, u(\tau)\, d\tau.$$

and

$$Y(\tau)\, u(\tau) = y^1(\tau)\, u_1(\tau) + \cdots + y^r(\tau)\, u_r(\tau),$$

where $y^j(\tau)$ is the jth column vector in $Y(\tau)$, the jth component of the control u_j has no effect when $y^j(\tau) = 0$. Now $y^j(\tau) = X^{-1}(\tau)\, b^j(\tau)$, where $b^j(\tau)$ is the jth column vector of $B(\tau)$, and therefore, $y^j(\tau) = 0$ is equivalent to $b^j(\tau) = 0$. If B is a constant matrix, then $y^j(\tau) = 0$ for any τ means $b^j = 0$, and the jth component of control never has an effect. We might as well remove b^j from B (reduce r by one). Thus, the distinctions we are about to make by adding the adjective "essential" are not really significant when B is a constant matrix. We could also restrict admissible control to $u_j(\tau) = 0$ when $b^j(\tau) = 0$, but while reasonable to do so from the point of view of applications it is not essential and we prefer another tactic.

We will say that two controls u^1 and u^2 are *essentially equal* on $[0, t^*]$ if for each $j = 1, \ldots, r$, $u_j^1(t) = u_j^2(t)$ almost everywhere on $[0, t^*]$ where $b^j(t) \neq 0$; that is the corresponding components of control are equal whenever they are effective. The control to reach q in time t^* is said to be *essentially unique* if $q = y(t^*; u^1) = y(t^*; u^2)$ implies u^1 is essentially equal to u^2. A control will be said to be *essentially bang-bang* on $[0, t^*]$ if it is essentially equal on $[0, t^*]$ to a bang-bang control; that is, if $\{t; |u_j(t)| < 1, b^j(t) \neq 0, t \in [0, t^*]\}$ has measure zero for each $j = 1, \ldots, r$. Whenever the control is effective it is bang-bang.

EXERCISE 14.1. Show that essential equality is an equivalence relation.

EXERCISE 14.2. Show, with respect to reaching q in time t^*, that essential uniqueness of control implies uniqueness of trajectory.

It is quite easy to see (Exercise 14.2) that uniqueness of control implies uniqueness of the trajectory. The converse is true but not so obvious. Consider, for instance the simple system ($n = r = 2$)

$$\dot{y}_1 = u_1 + u_2,$$
$$\dot{y}_2 = u_1 + u_2 \qquad -1 \leqq u_i \leqq 1, \quad i = 1, 2.$$

Now the controls

$$u^1 = \begin{pmatrix} 1 \\ 0 \end{pmatrix} \quad \text{and} \quad u^2 = \begin{pmatrix} 0 \\ 1 \end{pmatrix}$$

which are clearly different controls, bring the system in unit time from the origin to $(1, 1)$ but yield the same trajectory. However the trajectory to reach $(1, 1)$ in unit time is not unique.

Theorem 14.1 The following are equivalent:
  (1) uniqueness of the trajectory to reach q in time t^*;
  (2) the controls to reach q in time t^* are essentially bang-bang;
  (3) the control to reach q in time t^* is essentially unique.

Proof. We will show that $(1) \Rightarrow (2) \Rightarrow (3)$ and, since obviously $(3) \Rightarrow (1)$ (Exercise 14.2), this will complete the proof. We may assume that $q \in \mathcal{R}(t^*)$ since otherwise the statements are true vacuously.

$(1) \Rightarrow (2)$: We show that not (2) implies not (1). Assume that q can be reached in time t^* by a control u^* which is not essentially bang-bang; that is, for some $j = 1, \dots, r$ the set

$$E_j = \{t; |u_j^*(t)| < 1, b_j(t) \neq 0, t \in [0, t^*]\}$$

has positive measure and $q = y(t^*; u^*)$. By the bang-bang principle (Theorem 12.1) there is a bang-bang control u_j for which

$$\int_0^{t^*} y^j(t)\, u_j(t)\, dt = \int_0^{t^*} y^j(t)\, u_j^*(t)\, dt.$$

Define $u_i = u_i^*$ for $i \neq j$ and take $u_j(t)$ as above. Then $q = y(t^*; u) = y(t^*; u^*)$ but

$$Y(t)[u(t) - u^*(t)] = y^j(t)\, [u_j(t) - u_j^*(t)] \neq 0$$

on E_j. Therefore, since $y(t; u)$ is absolutely continuous, we have for some $t_1 \in (0, t^*)$ that $y(t_1; u) \neq y(t_1; u^*)$.

$(2) \Rightarrow (3)$. Assume that (2) is true and that u^1 and u^2 are admissible controls that bring the system to q in time t^*. Then $u = \frac{1}{2}u^1 + \frac{1}{2}u^2$ is an admissible control that brings the system to q in time t^*. Since u, u^1, and u^2 are by assumption essentially bang-bang, it must be that u^1 is essentially equal to u^2. Therefore (2) implies (3), and, since it is clear that $(3) \Rightarrow (1)$, this completes the proof of the theorem.

This theorem shows us, in addition to the fact that these types of uniqueness are the same, that an essentially unique control is always essentially bang-bang. We show next that what was observed at the beginning of this section (Figure 14.1) is in general true (see Section 8 for the definition of an extreme point).

Theorem 14.2   A point q is reached in time t^* by a unique trajectory if and only if q is an extreme point of $\mathcal{R}(t^*)$.

Proof. Assume that there are controls u^1 and u^2 and a $t_1 \in (0, t^*)$ such that $p_1 = y(t_1; u^1) \neq y(t_1; u^2) = p_2$ and $q^* = y(t^*; u^1) = y(t^*, u^2)$. Define

$$q_1 = p_1 + (q - p_2)$$

and

$$q_2 = p_2 + (q - p_1).$$

Then q_1 may be attained by using control u^1 on $[t_0, t_1]$ and control u^2 on $(t_1, t^*]$; q_2 may be attained in a similar fashion. Thus $q_1 \in \mathcal{R}(t^*)$, $q_2 \in \mathcal{R}(t^*)$, $q_1 \neq q_2$, and $q = \frac{1}{2}q_1 + \frac{1}{2}q_2$. Hence q is not an extreme point of $\mathcal{R}(t^*)$.

Conversely, assume that q is not an extreme point of $\mathcal{R}(t^*)$. If q is not in $\mathcal{R}(t^*)$, then it cannot be reached in time t^*. If q is in $\mathcal{R}(t^*)$, then $q = \frac{1}{2}q_1 + \frac{1}{2}q_2$ with $q_1 \neq q_2$ and $q_1, q_2 \in \mathcal{R}(t^*)$. By the bang-bang principle (Theorem 12.1) there are bang-bang controls u^1 and u^2 such that $q_1 = y(t^*; u^1)$ and $q_2 = y(t^*; u^2)$. Then $q = y(t^*; \frac{1}{2}u^1 + \frac{1}{2}u^2)$. Now it cannot be that $u = \frac{1}{2}u^1 + \frac{1}{2}u^2$ is essentially bang-bang. This would mean that $u^1(t)$ is essentially equal to $u^2(t)$ almost everywhere on $[0, t^*]$ which would imply $y(t^*; u^1) = y(t^*; u^2)$. Hence q^* can be reached by a control that is not essentially bang-bang and by Theorem 14.1 the trajectory to q^* is not unique. This completes the proof.

This theorem states that what we saw in the simple example at the beginning of this section is in general true. The point y^0 (Fig. 14.1) is not an extreme point of $\mathcal{R}(t^*)$ and the trajectory to reach y^0 in time t^* is not unique. The point y^1 is an extreme point of $\mathcal{R}(t^*)$ (it is also exposed), and the trajectory reaching y^1 in time t^* is unique. For further results along these lines see [11].

15. Unique Determination of the Control by the Necessary Condition. Normal Systems

In the previous section we answered the question of uniqueness of the trajectory in terms of a geometric property of the reachable set. Thus, if for the problem of time optimal control the minimum time is t^*, then $w(t^*)$ is on the boundary of $\mathcal{R}(t^*)$, and if $w(t^*)$ is an extreme point of $\mathcal{R}(t^*)$, then the control to reach $w(t^*)$ in time t^* is essentially unique and essentially bang-bang. This, as we shall see in this section, does not answer the more important question (certainly more important from the point of view of developing computational methods of computing optimal controls) of when the optimal control is uniquely determined by the necessary condition for optimal control (Theorem 13.2) which states that

$$u^*(t) = \operatorname{sgn}[\eta' Y(t)], \quad \eta \neq 0, \tag{15.1}$$

where η is some nonzero vector [an outward normal to a support plane $\pi(\eta)$ of $\mathcal{R}(t^*)$ at $w(t^*)$].

This necessary condition, as we have seen by examples, may give no information about the optimal control and certainly will not, in general, determine a unique control. The condition (15.1) states that

$$u_j^*(t) = \operatorname{sgn}[\eta' y^j(t)] = \operatorname{sgn}[\eta' X^{-1}(t) b^j(t)] \tag{15.2}$$

on $[0, t_j^*]$ for $j = 1, \ldots, r$ where $y^j(t)$ and $b^j(t)$ are the jth column vectors of $Y(t)$ and $B(t)$. When $\eta' y^j(t) = 0$ Eq. 15.2 gives no information about $u_j(t)$. If $b^j(t) = 0$, this doesn't matter because then the control has no effect and $u_j(t)$ can be taken to be any value between -1 and 1

and might as well be taken to be zero. But $\eta' y^j(t)$ can vanish when $u_j(t)$ is effective and this does matter. Let

$$E_j(\eta) = \{\, t; \eta' y^j(t) = 0,\ b^j(t) \neq 0,\ t \in [0, t^*]\,\}. \qquad (15.3)$$

If $E_j(\eta)$ has measure zero, then $u_j^*(t)$ is uniquely determined on $[0, t^*]$ by (15.2) whenever the control is effective. We shall say that Eq. 15.1 *essentially determines* u^* on $[0, t^*]$ if $u^1(t) = \text{sgn}[\eta' Y(t)]$ and $u^2(t) = \text{sgn}[\eta' Y(t)]$ implies u^1 and u^2 are essentially equal on $[0, t^*]$. When this is true u^* will be essentially *bang-bang*. Thus, u^* *is essentially determined by* (15.1) *if and only if* $E_j(\eta)$ *has measure zero for each* $j = 1, \ldots, n$. When this is the case the control will be essentially unique and the point $q^* = y(t^*; u^*)$ will be an extreme point (Theorem 14.2).

Actually, as we shall show in the next theorem, q^* must be an exposed point. Thus there is only a slight difference between uniqueness of the trajectory and the control being essentially determined by the necessary condition (15.1). The distinction arises only when q^* is an extreme point but is not exposed (see Exercise 15.3).

Theorem 15.1   The control u^* to reach q^* in time t^* is essentially determined on $[0, t^*]$ by $u^*(t) = \text{sgn}[\eta' Y(t)]$ for some $\eta \neq 0$ if and only if $q^* = y(t^*; u^*)$ is an exposed point of $\mathcal{R}(t^*)$.

Proof. Assume first that u^* is essentially determined on $[0, t^*]$ by $u^*(t) = \text{sgn}[\eta' Y(t)]$. From Lemma 13.1 we know that q^* is a boundary point of $\mathcal{R}(t^*)$ with η an outward normal to a support plane $\pi(\eta)$ of $\mathcal{R}(t^*)$ at q^* and that points on this support plane can be reached in time t^* only by controls of this form. Since any other control of this form is essentially equal to u^*, q^* is the only point of $\mathcal{R}(t^*)$ on $\pi(\eta)$. Therefore q^* is an exposed point. Conversely, assume that q^* is an exposed point of $\mathcal{R}(t^*)$. Then for some support plane $\pi(\eta)$ of $\mathcal{R}(t^*)$ through q^*, q^* is the only point of $\mathcal{R}(t^*)$ on $\pi(\eta)$, and $q^* = y(t^*; u^*)$ where $u^*(t) = \text{sgn}[\eta' Y(t)]$ on $[0, t^*]$ (Lemma 13.1). Now controls of the form $\text{sgn}[\eta' Y(t)]$ reach $\pi(\eta)$ in time t^* (Lemma 13.1), and since q^* is exposed must reach q^*. An exposed point is an extreme point and by Theorem 14.2 the control to reach q^* in time t^* is essentially unique. Hence u^* is essentially determined by $u^*(t) = \text{sgn}[\eta' Y(t)]$ on $[0, t^*]$, and this completes the proof.

EXERCISE 15.1. Let $N(q)$ denote the cone of unit outward normals to support hyperplanes to $\mathcal{R}(t_1)$ at a point q belonging to the boundary of $\mathcal{R}(t_1)$ and let u be such that $y(t_1; u) = q$. Show that $N(y(t; u)) \supset N(q)$ if $t \leq t_1$. When $N(q_1)$ consists of more than one vector we say that $\mathcal{R}(t_1)$ has a *corner* at q. Hence conclude, if $\mathcal{R}(t^*)$ has no corners, that $\mathcal{R}(t)$ has no "corners" for $t > t^*$.

EXERCISE 15.2. Show that the attainable set $\mathcal{A}(t)$ [and hence $\mathcal{R}(t)$] for

$$\dot{x}_1 = x_2$$
$$x_2 = -x_1 + u, \qquad x(0) = 0, \quad |u(t)| \leq 1,$$

has "corners" for $0 < t < \pi$ and is a circle of radius 2, centered at the origin, for $t = \pi$. Hence conclude that $\mathcal{A}(t)$ has no corners for $t \geq \pi$.

EXERCISE 15.3 Show for the system

$$\dot{x}_1 = x_2, \qquad \dot{x}_2 = -x_1 + u, \qquad 0 \leq t \leq \pi,$$
$$\dot{x}_1 = 0, \qquad \dot{x}_2 = u, \qquad t > \pi,$$

with $|u(t)| \leq 1$, that $\mathcal{R}(t)$ has points for $t > \pi$ which are extreme but not exposed and that for these points the control (which is essentially unique and essentially bang-bang) is not essentially determined by $\mathrm{sgn}[\eta' Y(t)]$. In fact, show that this necessary condition for these points gives no information about the control u.

EXERCISE 15.4. Prove Theorem 15.1 directly without making use of Theorem 14.2 and the bang-bang principle.

Again referring to the example at the beginning of Section 14 and to Fig. 14.1 the vertex y^1 is an exposed point and the control u^* to reach y^1 is uniquely determined by $u^* = \mathrm{sgn}[\eta' Y(t)]$, where

$$\eta = \begin{pmatrix} \eta_1 \\ \eta_2 \end{pmatrix}$$

for any $\eta_1 > 0$, $\eta_2 > 0$. All that is necessary is that $\pi(\eta)$ be a support plane that contains no point of $\mathcal{R}(t^*)$ other than y^1. *Uniqueness of the control and its being determined uniquely by the necessary condition* $u^*(t) = \mathrm{sgn}[\eta' Y(t)]$ *have nothing to do with uniqueness of the direction* η. Exercise 15.3 gives an example where optimal control is essentially unique, and therefore essentially bang-bang, and yet the necessary condition gives no information about the form of the optimal control to reach points that are extreme but not exposed.

We will say that the system

$$\dot{x} = A(t) \, x + B(t) \, u \qquad (15.4)$$

is *essentially normal* on $[0, t^*]$ if $E_j(\eta)$ [Eq. (15.3)] has measure zero for each $j = 1, \ldots, r$ and each $\eta \neq 0$. If the system (15.4) is essentially normal on $[0, t^*]$ for each $t^* > 0$ we say simply that the system (15.4) is *essentially normal*.

Hence we see that if (15.4) *is essentially normal on* $[0, t^*]$, *then on* $[0, t^*]$ *optimal control is essentially unique, is essentially bang-bang, and is essentially determined by the necessary condition* (15.1). *Conversely, it is essentially normal on* $[0, t^*]$ *only if, for each* $\eta \neq 0$, $u(t) = \text{sgn}[\eta' \, Y(t)]$ *essentially determines* $u(t)$ *on* $[0, t^*]$.

As an immediate consequence of Theorem 15.2 (see Section 9 for the definition of strict convexity) we have:

Corollary 15.1 The system (15.4) is essentially normal on $[0, t]$ if and only if $\mathscr{R}(t^*)$ is strictly convex.

A stronger concept of normality is that of a "normal" system, and we introduce this concept since again the adjective "essential" has no real significance when B is a constant matrix. Also we want later on to compare proper and normal systems. Define

$$G_j(\eta) = \{t; \, \eta' y^j(t) = 0, \, t \in [0, t^*]\}.$$

We say that the system (15.4) is *normal on* $[0, t^*]$ if $G_j(\eta)$ has measure zero for each $j = 1, \ldots, r$ and each $\eta \neq 0$. If the system (15.4) is normal for each $t^* > 0$ we say simply that the system (15.4) is *normal*. Thus, *if a system is normal, control is always effective and optimal control is unique, bang-bang, and uniquely determined by the necessary condition* (15.1). Note also, if a system is normal, that if $[\eta' Y(t)]_j = \eta' y^j(t)$ vanishes on a set of positive measure for any $j = 1, \ldots, r$, then $\eta = 0$. Also it is clear, since $E_j(\eta) \subset G_j(\eta)$, that normal implies essentially normal.

EXERCISE 15.5. Let A and B be constant matrices. Then if (15.2) is normal on $[0, t^*]$ for any $t^* > 0$, it is a normal system.

To sum up what we have learned note that if a point q^* of $R(t^*)$ is exposed, then the trajectory $y(t; u^*)$ to q^* is unique and the control is essentially bang-bang and essentially unique. Moreover, u^* is essentially determined by $\operatorname{sgn}[\eta' Y(t)]$ for some $\eta \neq 0$.

If the system (15.4) is not essentially normal, there will be an $\eta \neq 0$ and j such that $E_j(\eta)$ has positive measure. In this case different control components u_j on $E_j(\eta)$ yield different trajectories but if two controls u^1 and u^2 differ only in their jth component on $E_j(\eta)$ then $\eta \cdot y(t^*; u^1) = \eta \cdot y(t^*; u^2)$, although $y(t^*; u^1) \neq y(t^*; u^2)$. This shows that $y(t^*; u^1)$ and $y(t^*; u^2)$ belong to the intersection of $R(t^*)$ with its support plane determined by η. This intersection is the intersection of two convex sets, and hence is convex. This means that when the system is not essentially normal on $[0, t^*]$ there is a "flat spot" on the boundary of $R(t^*)$.

We have also shown that if the system (15.4) is essentially normal, then boundary points of $R(t^*)$ can, and can only, be reached by a control that is essentially bang-bang. The value of the control component u_j has no effect on the trajectory when $y^j(t) = 0$. We may choose it to be one in absolute value for such values of t and again conclude that all boundary points of $R(t^*)$ may be attained with bang-bang control. If the system is *not* essentially normal, we cannot use the formula $u^*(t) = \operatorname{sgn}[\eta' Y(t)]$ to conclude that points q^* which belong to a "flat spot" of the boundary of $\mathscr{R}(t^*)$ may be reached by bang-bang controls. Here we must appeal to the bang-bang principle, Theorem 12.1, which shows that *all* points of $\mathscr{R}(t^*)$ may be reached by bang-bang control.

Theorems 14.1 and 14.2 show that essential uniqueness of control to reach a point q^*, uniqueness of the trajectory to q^*, and q^* being an extreme point are all equivalent. But uniqueness of the trajectory may not imply that the essentially unique control to reach q^* is essentially determined by $\operatorname{sgn}[\eta' Y(t)]$ for an $\eta \neq 0$. This can happen when q^* is an extreme point of $\mathscr{R}(t^*)$ but is not an exposed point (Exercise 15.3). Theorems 14.1 and 14.2 seem to be somewhat deeper results than Theorem 15.1 in that their proofs seem to require the bang-bang principle which in turn is equivalent to Liapunov's theorem on the range of a vector measure (Theorem 8.2), whereas the proof of Theorem 15.1 can be made quite elementary (Exercise 15.4).

Figure 15.1 illustrates in the plane some of the geometric possibilities

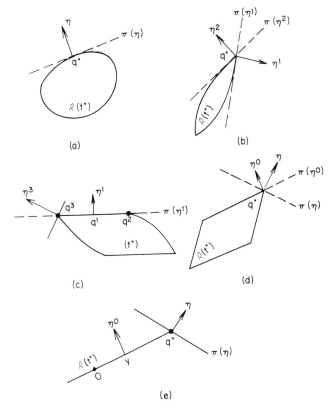

Fig. 15.1.

for the reachable set. In Fig. 15.1a the set R^* is strictly convex and at each boundary point q^* there is a unique support plane $\pi(\eta)$ with unique outward normal η. The control u^* to reach q^* in time t^* is uniquely determined by $u^*(t) = \text{sgn}[\eta' Y(t)]$ and is essentially bang-bang. The system giving rise to this $\mathscr{R}(t^*)$ must be essentially normal on $[0, t^*]$. In Fig. 15.1b the set $\mathscr{R}(t^*)$ is strictly convex and the control system for this $\mathscr{R}(t^*)$ is also essentially normal. It differs from Fig. 15.1a in that there are points q^* where the support plane is not unique. However, each support plane $\pi(\eta)$ to $\mathscr{R}(t^*)$ at q^* contains no point of $\mathscr{R}(t^*)$ other than q^* and the control u^* for which $q^* = y(t^*, u^*)$ is uniquely determined by $u^*(t) = \text{sgn}[\eta' Y(t)]$, where η is any of these outward normals at q^*. The point q_1 of Fig. 15.1c is not an extreme point and this is an exceptional (singular) case. Although $\pi(\eta^1)$ is unique, the control to q_1 is not unique and there are an infinity of admissible trajectories reaching q_1 in time t^*. However, the bang-bang principle (Theorem 12.1) assures us that there is at least one bang-bang control which brings the system to q^* in time t^*. The point q_2 of Fig. 15.1c is an extreme point of $\mathcal{R}(t^*)$ that is not exposed. The support plane $\pi(\eta^1)$ is unique, the control that brings the system to q_2 in time t^* is essentially unique, is essentially bang-bang, but *not* essentially determined by $\text{sgn}[\eta' Y(t)]$ on $[0, t^*]$. Here the control system for $\mathcal{R}(t^*)$ is not normal on $[0, t^*]$. The situation at q^* in Fig. 15.1d is similar to that at q^* in Fig. 15.1b except that there are support planes such as $\pi(\eta^0)$ at $q^* = y(t^*; u^*)$ for which the control u^* is not essentially determined by $\text{sgn}[\eta^0 Y(t)]$ on $[0, t^*]$ but is essentially determined by $\text{sgn}[\eta' Y(t)]$ with η as shown in Fig. 15.1d. In Fig. 15.1e the dimension of $\mathcal{R}(t^*)$ is less than n ($n \geq 2$) and $\eta^0 Y(t) = 0$ on $[0, t^*]$. Thus, for each point $y(t^*; u)$ of $\mathcal{R}(t^*)$, although it is true that $u(t) = \text{sgn}[\eta^0 Y(t)]$, this gives no information about the control u. The point q^* is an exposed point and what happens here does not differ essentially from that at q^* in Fig. 15.1d.

EXERCISE 15.6. Show that: (a) If $y(t^*, u^*)$ is an extreme (exposed) point of $\mathcal{R}(t^*)$ then $y(t, u^*)$ is an extreme (exposed) point of $\mathcal{R}(t)$ for each $t \in [0, t^*]$. (b) $\mathcal{R}(t^*)$ strictly convex implies $\mathcal{R}(t)$ is strictly convex for all $t \in [0, t^*]$.

EXERCISE 15.7. Show that: If the system (15.4) is normal on $[0, t^*]$, then the origin is an interior point of $\mathcal{R}(t^*)$.

16. Normality of Systems with Constant Coefficients

Here our system is
$$\dot{x} = Ax + Bu, \tag{16.1}$$
where A and B are constant matrices. We will also assume that no column vector b^j of B is zero so that each component of control is

always effective and we have no need for the adjective "essential." For this system

$$X(t) = e^{At} \quad \text{and} \quad Y(t) = e^{-At}B,$$

and these are real analytic functions. Hence $[n' Y(t)]_j = \eta' y^j(t) = \eta' e^{-At} b^j$ either is identically zero or has a finite number of zeros on each finite interval. Therefore system (16.1) *is normal if and only if* $\eta' e^{-At} b^j \equiv 0$ *for some* $j = 1, \ldots, r$ *implies* $\eta = 0$.

We then have immediately that *if the system* (16.1) *is normal, optimal control* (if it exists) *is always unique and bang-bang, and is determined by the necessary condition of Theorem 13.2 for some* $\eta \neq 0$.

Now when A and B are constant matrices we can characterize normality directly in terms of these two matrices. Evaluating the identity $\eta' e^{-At} b^j \equiv 0$ and its derivatives at $t = 0$ implies $\eta' b^j = 0$, $\eta' A b^j = 0, \ldots, \eta' A^{n-1} b^j = 0$, we see that (16.1) is normal if b^j, $A b^j, \ldots$, $A^{n-1} b^j$ are linearly independent for each $j = 1, \ldots, r$. We now show that the converse of this is true.

Theorem 16.1 The system (16.1) is normal if and only if for each $j = 1, \ldots, r$ the vectors b^j, $A b^j, \ldots, A^{n-1} b^j$ are linearly independent.

Proof. The sufficiency of the condition was shown above. To prove the necessity assume for some j that the vectors b^j, $A b^j, \ldots, A^{n-1} b^j$ are linearly dependent, which implies for some nonzero vector η that

$$\eta' b^j = \eta' A b^j = \cdots = \eta' A^{n-1} b^j = 0.$$

Let

$$v(t) = \eta' e^{-At} b^j.$$

Then

$$(D^k v)(t) = \eta'(-A)^k e^{-At} b^j, \quad \text{where} \quad D = d/dt.$$

Let $\varphi(-\lambda)$ be the characteristic polynomial of A. By the Hamilton–Cayley theorem $\varphi(-A) = 0$. Hence $\varphi(D)v = \eta'(\varphi(D)e^{-At})b^i = \eta'(\varphi(-A)e^{-At})b^i = 0$; that is, v satisfies $\varphi(D)v = 0$ and, at $t = 0$, $D^k v = 0$, $k = 0, \ldots, n - 1$. By the existence-uniqueness theorem of differential equations $v(t) \equiv 0$. Hence (16.1) is not normal and this completes the proof.

The general second-order linear differential equation with constant coefficients

$$\ddot{x}_1 + 2b_0 \dot{x}_1 + c_0 x_1 = u(t)),$$

which is the problem Bushaw studied, is equivalent to

$$\dot{x}_1 = x_2$$
$$\dot{x}_2 = -c_0 x_1 - 2b_0 x_2 + u(t).$$

Here

$$A = \begin{pmatrix} 0 & 1 \\ -c_0 & -2b_0 \end{pmatrix}, \qquad b = \begin{pmatrix} 0 \\ 1 \end{pmatrix}, \qquad \text{and} \qquad Ab = \begin{pmatrix} 1 \\ -2b_0 \end{pmatrix}.$$

Since b and Ab are linearly independent this system is normal. Therefore optimal control is unique and bang-bang.

More generally the nth-order equation

$$\varphi(D)x_1 = u(t), \tag{16.2}$$

where $\varphi(\lambda) = \lambda^n + a_1 \lambda^{n-1} + \cdots + a_n$ and $D = d/dt$ is normal (Exercise 16.1) and, in fact, every normal autonomous system with $r = 1$ is equivalent to a system of the form (16.2) [Exercise (16.5)]; that is, if $\dot{x} = Ax + bu$ is normal then there is a change of coordinates $y = Qx$ such that

$$QAQ^{-1} = \begin{pmatrix} 0 & 1 & 0 & . & . & . & 0 \\ 0 & 0 & 1 & . & . & . & 0 \\ . & & & & & & . \\ . & & & & & & . \\ . & & & & & & . \\ 0 & . & & . & . & 0 & 1 \\ -a_n & -a_{n-1} & . & . & . & . & -a_1 \end{pmatrix}, \qquad Qb = \begin{pmatrix} 0 \\ \vdots \\ \vdots \\ 0 \\ 1 \end{pmatrix},$$

and the original system is equivalent to $\varphi(D)y_1 = u.$

EXERCISE 16.1. Show that $\varphi(D)x_1 = u$ is normal.

EXERCISE 16.2. For $\dot{x} = Ax + bu$ $(r = 1)$ show that the concept of normality is invariant under a linear change of coordinates $y = Qx$.

EXERCISE 16.3. The nth order system $\dot{x} = Ax$ is equivalent to an nth-order equation $\varphi(D)y_1 = 0$ if and only if there exists a vector a such that $a, aA, \ldots, aA^{n-1}$ are linearly independent.

EXERCISE 16.4. If $b, Ab, \ldots, A^{n-1}b$ are linearly independent and $a \neq 0$ is orthogonal to $b, Ab, \ldots, A^{n-2}b$, then $a, aA, \ldots, aA^{n-1}$ are linearly independent.

EXERCISE 16.5. Show that $\dot{x} = Ax + bu$ is normal if and only if it is equivalent to an nth-order equation of the form $\varphi(D)y_1 = u$.

EXERCISE 16.6. Show that if A has two (or more) linearly independent eigenvectors corresponding to the same eigenvalue, then $\dot{x} = Ax + bu$ cannot be normal.

EXERCISE 16.7. Show that the system (16.1) is normal if and only if the functions $y_1^j(t), y_2^j(t), \ldots, y_n^j(t)$ are linearly independent on some interval of positive length for each $j = 1, \ldots, r$. ($Y(t) = (y_i^j(t))$).

17. Sufficient Conditions for Optimal Control for a Special Problem. Proper Systems

We wish to confine ourselves for the moment to the special problem of reaching the origin in minimum time ($z(t) \equiv 0$, $w(t) \equiv -x^0$). Thus for the fundamental control system

$$\dot{x} = A(t)\, x + B(t)\, u(t), \quad x(0) = x^0, \tag{17.1}$$

we may consider x to be the error in control, and what we wish to do is to reduce this control error to zero in the shortest possible time. Now reaching the origin in time t corresponds to $-x^0 \in \mathcal{R}(t)$ and the reachable set $\mathcal{R}(t)$, being symmetric about the origin, is therefore the set of all initial states from which it is possible by admissible control to go to the origin in time t. the necessary condition for optimal control (Theorem 13.2) is derived from and is equivalent to the fact that $-x_0$

is on the boundary of $\mathcal{R}(t^*)$ where t^* is the minimum time. Now it is quite clear that without further restrictions on the system (17.1) a point $-x_0$ can remain on the boundary of the reachable set $\mathcal{R}(t)$ over an interval of time—this means that over this interval of time $\mathcal{R}(t)$ is not "expanding" at $-x_0$. Therefore even for this simple problem of reaching the origin the necessary conditions for optimal control may not be sufficient. We will say that the reachable set $\mathcal{R}(t)$ is *expanding at time* t^* if $\mathcal{R}(t)$ is contained in the interior of $\mathcal{R}(t^*)$ for all $0 \le t < t^*$ If $\mathcal{R}(t)$ is expanding for all $t^* > 0$ we will say simply that $\mathcal{R}(t)$ is *expanding*. Hence if $\mathcal{R}(t)$ is expanding at time t^* and $-x_0$ is on the boundary of $\mathcal{R}(t^*)$, then t^* is the minimum time it will take to go from x^0 to the origin, and *any control that does this will be optimal*. Note that $\mathcal{R}(t)$ expanding does *not* imply that $\mathcal{A}(t)$ will be expanding. This is not to be expected since $\mathcal{A}(t) = X(t)\,(x^0 + \mathcal{R}(t))$.

Let us suppose that there is a control u^* of the form

$$u^*(t) = \operatorname{sgn}[\eta' Y(t)] \qquad \text{for some} \quad \eta \ne 0 \qquad (17.2)$$

that brings the system (17.1) from x^0 to the origin in time t^*. Then $-x_0$ will be a point on the boundary of $\mathcal{R}(t^*)$ and if $\mathcal{R}(t^*)$ is expanding at time t^* then t^* is the minimum time and u^* is an optimal control. [In terms of $\mathcal{A}(t)$ this is simply saying that the origin is not in $\mathcal{A}(t)$ for $t < t^*$.] From this we can conclude:

Theorem 17.1 (Sufficiency Condition). If a control u^* of the form (17.2) brings a system from a point x^0 to the origin in time t^*, and if $\mathcal{R}(t)$ is expanding at time t^*, then u^* is an optimal control.

Of course what we would like to have are some criteria for when the system (17.1) is expanding, and to be of practical value we want criteria that can be checked computationally from a knowledge of the matrices A and B.

As a first step in this direction we give a characterization of when $\mathcal{R}(t)$ is expanding. We shall say that the system (17.1) is *proper on an interval* $[t_0, t_1]$ if $\eta' Y(t) \equiv 0$ a.e. on $[t_0, t_1]$ implies $\eta = 0$. If (17.1) is proper on $[t_0, t_0 + \delta]$ for each $\delta > 0$ we say the system is *proper at time* t_0. If (17.1) is proper on each interval $[t_0, t_1]$, $t_1 > t_0 \ge 0$, we say simply that the system is *proper*.

Theorem 17.2 $\mathscr{R}(t)$ is expanding at time t^* if and only if the system (17.1) is proper on $[t^* - \delta, t^*]$ for each $\delta > 0$.

Proof. Assume that (17.1) is proper on $[t^* - \delta, t^*]$ for each $\delta > 0$ and let $q = y(t_1, u)$ be any point in $\mathscr{R}(t_1)$, $0 < t_1 < t^*$. Since $\mathscr{R}(t_1) \subset \mathscr{R}(t^*)$, $q \in \mathscr{R}(t^*)$. Suppose q is on the boundary of $\mathscr{R}(t^*)$. Let $\pi(\eta)$ be a support plane of $\mathscr{R}(t^*)$ at q with η an outward normal; i.e., $\eta'(p - q) \leq 0$ for all $p \in \mathscr{R}(t^*)$. Define

$$u^*(t) = \begin{cases} u(t), & 0 \leq t \leq t_1, \\ \operatorname{sgn}[\eta' Y(t)], & t_1 < t \leq t^*. \end{cases}$$

Then for $p = y(t^*; u^*) \in \mathscr{R}(t^*)$

$$\eta'(p - q) = \int_{t_1}^{t^*} \eta' Y(t) \, dt = \int_{t_1}^{t^*} \sum_{j=1}^{r} |\eta' Y(t)|_j \, dt > 0,$$

since the system is proper on $[t_1, t^*]$. This contradicts our assumption that q is on the boundary of $\mathscr{R}(t^*)$, and hence it is an interior point of $\mathscr{R}(t^*)$. Therefore $\mathscr{R}(t_1)$ is contained in the interior of $\mathscr{R}(t^*)$ for all $0 < t_1 < t^*$. Conversely, if (17.1) is not proper on $[t^* - \delta, t^*]$ for all $\delta > 0$, then $\eta' Y(t) \equiv 0$ a.e. on $[t^* - \delta, t^*]$ for some $\eta \neq 0$ and some $\delta > 0$. Let u^1 be any control satisfying $u^1(t) = \operatorname{sgn}[\eta' Y(t)]$ on $[0, t^* - \delta]$ and define

$$u^*(t) = \begin{cases} u^1(t), & 0 \leq t \leq t^* - \delta, \\ 0, & t^* - \delta < t \leq t^*. \end{cases}$$

Then u^* is of the form $\operatorname{sgn}[\eta' Y(t)]$ on $[0, t^*]$. From Lemma 13.1, $q = y(t^* - \delta; u^1) = y(t^*; u^*)$ is on the boundary of both $\mathscr{R}(t^* - \delta)$ and $\mathscr{R}(t^*)$. Therefore $\mathscr{R}(t^* - \delta^*)$ is not contained in the interior of $\mathscr{R}(t^*)$ for any $0 < \delta^* \leq \delta$ and $\mathscr{R}(t)$ is not expanding at t^*. This completes the proof.

Since the system (17.1) is proper if and only if it is proper on each interval $[t^* - \delta, t^*]$ for all $\delta > 0$ and t^*, we have immediately:

Corollary 17.1 $\mathscr{R}(t)$ is expanding if and only if the system (17.1) is proper.

Corollary 17.2   (Sufficiency Condition). If (17.1) is proper and, for some u^* of the form (17.2) and some $t^* \geq 0$, $x(t^*; u^*) = 0$, then u^* is an optimal control for the special problem $z(t) \equiv 0$ and t^* is the minimum time.

EXERCISE 17.1. Discuss sufficient conditions for optimal control when A is a constant matrix and the equations of motion of the moving target $z(t)$ are the same as the uncontrolled system ($\dot{z} = Az$).

It is quite clear that the concept of a normal system is much stronger than that of a proper system and *every normal system is proper*. Even when $r = 1$ there is a subtle difference between the concepts of normal and proper, and it is possible when $r = 1$ to have a system which is proper but not normal. This is a mathematical subtlety that we do not want to make too much out of. The definition of normality was motivated by Eq. (17.2). The system (17.1) is normal if $[\eta' Y(t)]_j = 0$ on a set of positive measure for any $j = 1, \ldots, r$ implies $\eta = 0$, and we know for normal systems that the control is determined almost everywhere by Eq. (17.2). Now it is possible to have a continuous function which vanishes on a set of positive measure but yet is not identically zero almost everywhere on any interval of positive length, and hence even for $r = 1$ it is possible to have a system which is proper but not normal. When A and B are constant (or analytic) matrices, then the concepts of normal and proper are the same when there is only one control component ($r = 1$).

For the autonomous system (A and B constant matrices)

$$\dot{x} = Ax + B u(t) \tag{17.3}$$

we can show:

Theorem 17.3   The autonomous system (17.3) is proper if and only if

$$\text{rank}[B, AB, \ldots, A^{n-1}B] = n. \tag{17.4}$$

Proof. Here proper is equivalent to $\eta' Y(t) \equiv 0$ implies $\eta = 0$ since $\eta' Y(t)$ is analytic. Now $\eta' Y(t) = \eta' e^{-At}B \equiv 0$ implies (by differentiating and setting $t = 0$) $\eta'B = 0$, $\eta'AB = 0$, $\ldots$, $\eta'A^{n-1}B = 0$. For $\eta \neq 0$ this implies (17.4) is not satisfied. We could proceed now just as we did in the proof of Theorem 16.1 but instead will use the Hamilton–Cayley theorem in a slightly different fashion. If (17.4) is not satisfied we can find an $\eta \neq 0$ such that $\eta'B = 0$, $\ldots$, $\eta'A^{n-1}B = 0$. By the Hamilton–Cayley theorem we can write A^n as a linear combintion of I, A, $\ldots$,

A^{n-1}, and hence, $\eta' A^n B = 0$. By a simple induction we obtain $\eta' A^k B = 0$ for all integers k, which implies $\eta' e^{-At} B \equiv 0$. This completes the proof.

EXAMPLE 17.1. The following system is proper but not normal:

$$\dot{x}_1 = -x_1 + u_1$$
$$\dot{x}_2 = -2x_2 + u_1 + u_2.$$

Here

$$A = \begin{pmatrix} -1 & 0 \\ 0 & -2 \end{pmatrix}, \qquad B = \begin{pmatrix} 1 & 0 \\ 1 & 1 \end{pmatrix}, \qquad b^1 = \begin{pmatrix} 1 \\ 1 \end{pmatrix},$$

$$b^2 = \begin{pmatrix} 0 \\ 1 \end{pmatrix}, \qquad Ab^1 = \begin{pmatrix} -1 \\ -2 \end{pmatrix}, \qquad Ab^2 = \begin{pmatrix} 0 \\ -2 \end{pmatrix}.$$

Since b^2 and Ab^2 are linearly dependent the system is not normal. However, the linear independence of b^1 and b^2 implies the system is proper. Hence the reachable set will not be strictly convex and the control will not be determined by the necessary condition.

When A and B are constant matrices, Theorem 17.3 and Corollary 17.2 give us a practical means of deciding when the necessary condition for optimal control (Theorem 13.2) is also sufficient for the special problem. Although Theorem 17.1 is a general sufficient condition, we do not as yet know how to check directly from a knowledge of $A(t)$ and $B(t)$ when $\mathscr{R}(t)$ is expanding at time t^*. In order to obtain a criterion of this type, we assume $A(t)$ has $(k - 2)$ continuous derivatives and $B(t)$ has $(k - 1)$ continuous derivatives. This means $Y(t)$ has $(k - 1)$ continuous derivatives. We first note that

$$\frac{dY(t)}{dt} = \dot{Y}(t) = DY(t) = X^{-1}(t)[-A(t) + D] B(t)$$

or

$$DY = X^{-1}[-A + D]B.$$

Defining $\Gamma = -A + D$ it is easy to see that

$$D^j Y = X^{-1} \Gamma^j B. \tag{17.5}$$

The operator Γ^j on the matrix function B is defined by induction: $\Gamma^j B = \Gamma(\Gamma^{j-1} B)$. For instance,

$$D^2 Y = D[X^{-1}(-A + D)]B = X^{-1}(-A + D)[(-A + D)B]$$
$$= X^{-1}(-A + D)^2 B = X^{-1}(A^2B - \dot{A}B - 2A\dot{B} + \ddot{B});$$

i.e.,

$$\Gamma^2 B = A^2 B - \dot{A}B - 2A\dot{B} + \ddot{B}$$

and

$$\Gamma^2 B(t_0) = A^2(t_0)\, B(t_0) - \dot{A}(t_0)\, B(t_0) - 2\, A(t_0)\, \dot{B}(t_0) + \ddot{B}(t_0).$$

In terms of this operator Γ we can now give a computable criterion that $\mathcal{R}(t)$ be expanding at time t^* and hence a sufficient condition for optimal control that depends only upon $A(t)$ and $B(t)$.

Theorem 17.4   Assume that A has $k - 2$ continuous derivatives at time $t^* > 0$ and that B has $k - 1$ continuous derivatives at t^*. If

$$\text{rank}[B(t^*),\ \Gamma B(t^*),\ \ldots,\ \Gamma^{k-1} B(t^*)] = n,$$

then $\mathcal{R}(t)$ is expanding at time t^*.

Proof. If $\mathcal{R}(t)$ is not expanding at time t^*, we have by Theorem 17.2 that there exists a nonzero vector η and a $\delta > 0$ such that $\eta' Y(t) \equiv 0$ on $[t^* - \delta, t^*]$. Differentiating and using (17.5) we obtain

$$\eta' X^{-1}(t)\, B(t) = \eta' X^{-1}(t)\, \Gamma\, B(t) = \cdots = \eta' X^{-1}(t)\, \Gamma^{k-1} B(t) \equiv 0$$

on $[t^* - \delta, t^*]$. Since $X^{-1}(t)$ is nonsingular, $\text{rank}[B(t^*), \ldots, \Gamma^{k-1} B(t^*)]$ $< n$, and this completes the proof.

Stated as a sufficient condition, we have from Theorems 17.1 and 17.4:

Corollary 17.3   The assumptions on A and B are as in Theorem 17.4. If a control u^* of the form (17.2) brings a system from a point x^0 to the origin in time t^* and if

$$\text{rank}[B(t^*),\ \Gamma B(t^*),\ \ldots,\ \Gamma^{k-1} B(t^*)] = n,$$

then u^* is optimal and t^* is the minimum time, for the special problem.

The condition which appears in Theorem 17.4 and Corollary 17.3 plays an important role in the study of the controllability of a system and will be studied in more detail in Section 19.

Up to this point in discussing the system (17.1) we have taken the initial time to be zero and the initial condition to be $x(0) = x^0$. It becomes convenient now to speak about an arbitrary initial time t_0 where t_0 is any nonnegative number. Let $X(t, t_0)$ be the matrix solution (see Section 10) of $\dot{x} = A(t) x$ satisfying $X(t_0, t_0) = I$, the identity matrix. Then in terms of our previous notation $X(t) = X(t, 0)$ and $X(t, t_0) = X(t) X^{-1}(t_0)$. The solution $x(t; t_0, x^0, u)$ of

$$\dot{x} = A(t) x + B(t) u(t), \qquad x(t_0) = x^0, \qquad (17.6)$$

is

$$x(t; t_0, x^0, u) = X(t) X^{-1}(t_0) x^0 + X(t) \int_{t_0}^{t} X^{-1}(\tau) B(\tau) u(\tau) d\tau$$

$$= X(t) X^{-1}(t_0) x^0 + X(t) y(t; t_0, u), \qquad (17.7)$$

where

$$y(t; t_0, u) = \int_{t_0}^{t} Y(\tau) u(\tau) d\tau.$$

Note that $y(t; t_0, u) = y(t; u) - y(t_0; u)$. Thus starting at time t_0 at x^0 and hitting the moving target $z(t)$ at some time $t \geq t_0$ corresponds to $z(t) = x(t; t_0, x^0, u)$. Define

$$\mathscr{A}(t, t_0) = \{x(t; t_0, x^0, u); u \in \Omega\},$$
$$\mathscr{R}(t, t_0) = \{y(t; t_0, u); u \in \Omega\},$$

and

$$w(t, t_0) = X^{-1}(t) z(t) - X^{-1}(t_0) x^0.$$

Then hitting the target at time t corresponds to $z(t) \in \mathscr{A}(t, t_0)$ or $w(t, t_0) \in \mathscr{R}(t, t_0)$. It is clear that everything proved previously about $\mathscr{R}(t)$ and $\mathscr{A}(t)$ can be extended to $\mathscr{R}(t, t_0)$ and $\mathscr{A}(t, t_0)$. For all $t \geq t_0$, $\mathscr{R}(t, t_0)$ and $\mathscr{A}(t, t_0)$ are convex, compact, and continuous functions of t and $\mathscr{R}(t, t_0)$ is symmetric about the origin. Note also that under the change of coordinates $x = X(t)y$ the differential equation for y is the same as before,

$$\dot{y} = Y(t) u(t) \qquad (17.8)$$

and $\mathscr{A}(t, t_0) = X(t)[X^{-1}(t_0) x^0 + \mathscr{R}(t, t_0)]$.

Now relative to an arbitrary initial time t_0 we have:

Theorem 17.5 The system (17.1) is proper on $[t_0, t_1]$, $t, > t_0$ if and only if the origin is an interior point of $\mathscr{R}(t_1, t_0)$.

Proof. The origin being on the boundary of $\mathscr{R}(t_1, t_0)$ is clearly equivalent to $n' Y(t) \equiv 0$ almost everywhere on the interval $[t_0, t_1]$ for some $\eta \neq 0$. This comples the proof since the origin is always in $\mathscr{R}(t_1, t_0)$.

Corollary 17.4 The system (17.1) is proper at t_0 if and only if the origin is an interior point of $\mathscr{R}(t, t_0)$ for each $t > t_0$.

Thus we see that the concept of a system being proper is related to a "controllability" property. Corollary 17.3 says, taking into consideration only the effect of the control, that at any given point of the state space and at any given time $t_0 \geq 0$ the system can be moved by admissible control in any desired direction. The special problem of bringing the system to the origin ($z(t) \equiv 0$) in finite time starting at time t_0 at x^0 is equivalent to $x^0 \in -X(t_0) \mathscr{R}(t, t_0) = X(t_0) \mathscr{R}(t, t_0)$ for some $t \geq t_0$. Hence we can conclude from Corollary 17.4 that given any initial time $t_0 \geq 0$ any any $t > t_0$ there is a neighborhood N of points about the origin from which starting at time t_0 it is possible using admissible control to bring the system to the origin in time t. Therefore, *if the uncontrolled system $\dot{x} = A(t)x$ is asymptotically stable and the system* (17.1) *is proper at time t_0, then there is for each initial state x^0 in R^n an admissible control u that brings the system to the origin in finite time*. If $\dot{x} = A(t) x$ is asymptotically stable, then it is asymptotically stable in the large. This means that starting from any initial state the system without control ($u = 0$) will arrive in the neighborhood N in finite time and then with admissible control can be brought to the origin in finite time. Hence in this case $\mathscr{R}(t_0) = \bigcup_{t \geq t_0} \mathscr{R}(t, t_0) = R^n$. If the system is proper, then $\mathscr{R}(t_0) = R^n$ for all $t_0 \geq 0$.

For the autonomous system

$$\dot{x} = Ax + B u(t) \tag{17.9}$$

we can prove a bit more and can include the case where the uncontrolled system is stable but not necessarily asymptotically stable. Note also that there may be multiple eigenvalues on the imaginary axis in which case the uncontrolled system is not stable and this, too, is included.

Theorem 17.6   If the system (17.9) is proper and no eigenvalue of A has a positive real part, then for each $x^0 \in R^n$ there is an admissible control that brings the system to the origin in finite time.

Proof.   What we want to show is that the set $\mathscr{R} = \bigcup_{t \geq 0} \mathscr{R}(t) = \{y(t; u);$ $u \in \Omega, t \geq 0\}$ is the whole space R^n. It is clear that $\mathscr{R}$ is convex, and we will show that $\mathscr{R}$ has the property stated in Exercise 17.3. Since the system is proper we know for any $\eta \neq 0$ that at least one component of $v(t) = \eta' Y(t) = \eta' e^{-At}B$ is not identically zero. We may assume $v_1(t) \not\equiv 0$. Assume that $\int_0^\infty |v_1(t)|\, dt < \infty$. Then the integral $\int_0^\infty v_1(t)\, dt$ converges, and we may define $w(t) = \int_t^\infty v_1(\tau)\, d\tau$. Since $v_1(t)$ satisfies $\varphi(-D) v_1(t) = 0$, where $D = d/dt$ and $\varphi(\lambda)$ is the characteristic equation of A, $w(t)$ satisfies $D\varphi(-D)w(t) = 0$. But $w(t) \to 0$ as $t \to \infty$ and this is a contradiction since $w(t) \not\equiv 0$ and the roots of $\lambda\varphi(-\lambda) = 0$ all have nonnegative real parts. Therefore $\int_0^\infty |v_1(t)|\, dt = \infty$. Hence with $u(t) = \operatorname{sgn}[\eta' e^{-At}B]$, $\eta' y(t, u) \to \infty$ as $t \to \infty$, and this completes the proof since this implies $\mathscr{R} = R^n$.

EXERCISE 17.2.   Show that $\mathscr{R} = \bigcup_{t \geq 0} \mathscr{R}(t)$ is convex. If (17.1) is proper, show that $\mathscr{R}$ is open.

EXERCISE 17.3.   Show that: If K is a convex set in R^n with the property that given any number $c > 0$ and any nonzero vector η in R^n there is a $y \in K$ such that $\eta' y > c$, then $K = R^n$.

EXERCISE 17.4.   Show that: If (17.9) is proper and the eigenvalues of A all lie on the imaginary axis, then given any two points x^0 and x^1 in R^n there is an admissible control that brings the system from x^0 to x^1 in finite time.

At this point we now have considerable information about optimal control and by looking at simple examples we can see how the theory can be used to obtain optimal control laws. In the three examples solved below we make use of the fact that the system is proper, and then use the sufficiency condition (Corollary 17.2). Then, since our systems are autonomous, we can start at the origin, integrate backwards with controls of the form $\operatorname{sgn}[\eta' Y(t)]$, and find all optimal trajectories into the origin. This procedure has quite limited applications, and for this reason we shall not bother with a detailed description. The theory does provide some general computational methods. Exercise 17.6 is the basis for one of these. For further information and references on computing optimal controls see [12], Appendix A.

EXAMPLE 17.2. We consider again (Example 13.1)

$$\ddot{x} + x = u, \quad |u| \leq 1,$$

which is equivalent to

$$\dot{x} = y,$$
$$\dot{y} = -x + u.$$

We want to reach the origin in minimum time. As we saw in Example 13.1, optimal control is of the form

$$u^*(t) = \text{sgn}[\sin(t + \delta)], \tag{17.10}$$

and, since the system is normal (and hence proper), any control of this form that brings the system into the origin is optimal. Since the eigenvalues of the uncontrolled system are $\pm i$, we also know that there is an optimal control for each initial state (x_0, y_0) in the (x, y) plane, and since the system is normal, this optimal control is uniquely determined by (17.10). When $u = \pm 1$, the trajectory in the (x, y) plane is a circle with center $(\pm 1, 0)$ with a clockwise direction of motion for increasing t (in time t the trajectory moves through an arc of the circle of angle t). With this information we can easily locate where optimal control changes sign. Thus, taking $-\pi \leq \delta \leq \pi$ in (17.10), we start at the origin with controls of the form (17.10), integrate backwards in time, and determine all optimal trajectories. With $0 < \delta \leq \pi$ we have (Fig. 17.1) starting at the origin that $u = 1$ and for decreasing t the optimal trajectory starts out counterclockwise along the semicircle with center at $(1, 0)$. At some point P_1 (at time $t = -\delta$) along this semicircle, $\sin(t + \delta)$ changes sign, and u switches to -1. The trajectory is now the semicircle with center at $(-1, 0)$ for $-\delta - \pi < t \leq -\delta$. At time $-\delta - \pi$ the point P_2 is reached and the control switches to $u = 1$, and so forth. Similarly, if $-\pi < \delta < 0$, the trajectory leaves the origin in decreasing time with $u = -1$ counterclockwise along the circle with center $(-1, 0)$. At a point such as Q_1 on the semicircle u changes sign. The trajectory is now the semicircle with center at $(1, 0)$ from Q_1 to

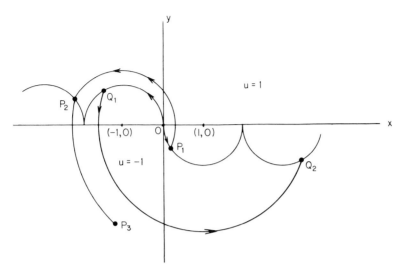

FIG. 17.1.

Q_2. At Q_2 it changes sign again, and so forth. It is thus not difficult to see that u changes sign along the chain of semicircles as shown in Fig. 17.1. Above the semicircles $u = -1$ and below $u = 1$. Note that this procedure has given an optimal control law as a function of the state (x, y) of the system ("feedback" or "closed loop" control), although our theory has had to do only with control as a function of t ("open loop") control.

EXAMPLE 17.3. Here we consider a system with two control components

$$\dot{x}_1 = -3x_1 - 2x_2 + u_1, \qquad |u_1| \leqq 1,$$
$$\dot{x}_2 = x_1 + u_2, \qquad\qquad |u_2| \leqq 1.$$

The eigenvalues of A are -1 and -2 and the linear change of coordinates

$$x_1 = 2z_1 - z_2,$$
$$x_2 = -z_1 + z_2$$

gives the equivalent system

$$\dot{z}_1 = -2z_1 + u_1 + u_2,$$
$$\dot{z}_2 = -z_2 + u_1 + 2u_2,$$

which is somewhat easier to deal with,

$$e^{At} = \begin{pmatrix} e^{-2t} & 0 \\ 0 & e^{-t} \end{pmatrix},$$

$$Y(t) = e^{-At}\begin{pmatrix} 1 & 1 \\ 1 & 2 \end{pmatrix} = \begin{pmatrix} e^{2t} & e^{2t} \\ e^t & 2e^t \end{pmatrix},$$

and

$$\eta' Y(t) = (\eta_1 e^{2t} + \eta_2 e^t, \eta_1 e^{2t} + 2\eta_2 e^t).$$

Clearly the system is normal. Therefore optimal control is uniquely determined by $u^*(t) = \text{sgn}[\eta' Y(t)]$ and for each point of the state space there is an optimal control (the eigenvalues are negative). To obtain the optimal trajectories we want to start at the origin and integrate backwards. To do this we replace t by $-\tau$, and have

$$dz_1/d\tau = 2z_1 - u_1 - u_2,$$
$$dz_2/d\tau = z_2 - u_1 - 2u_2,$$

where

$$u_1(\tau) = \text{sgn}(\eta_1 e^{-2\tau} + \eta_2 e^{-\tau}),$$
$$u_2(\tau) = \text{sgn}(\eta_1 e^{-2\tau} + 2\eta_2 e^{-\tau}).$$

Taking $\eta_1 + \eta_2 < 0$, $\eta_1 + 2\eta_2 < 0$, and $\eta_2 > 0$, we begin at the origin with $u_1 = -1$, $u_2 = -1$, and move along the parabola (Fig. 17.2)

$$\alpha: \quad \begin{aligned} z_1(\tau) &= e^{2\tau} - 1, \\ z_2(\tau) &= 3(e^\tau - 1). \end{aligned}$$

Now $u_2(\tau)$ will change sign at $\tau_1 = \ln(-\eta_1/2\eta_2)$ and $u_1(\tau)$ will change sign at $\tau_2 = \ln(-\eta_1/\eta_2)$. Hence $\tau_2 - \tau_1 = \ln 2$. Therefore starting at time $\tau = 0$ at the point $(z_1(\tau_1), z_2(\tau_1))$ of α with $u_1 = -1$, $u_2 = 1$, we leave α along the parabola

$$z_1(\tau) = z_1(\tau_1)e^{2\tau},$$
$$z_2(\tau) = z_2(\tau_1)e^\tau = (e^\tau - 1)$$

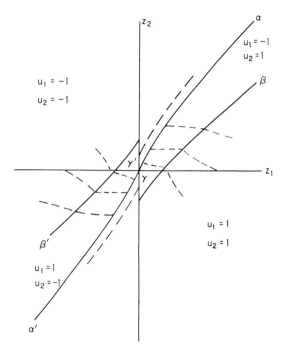

FIG. 17.2.

and u_1 changes signs at

$$z_1(\ln 2) = 4 \, z_1(\tau_1),$$
$$z_2(\ln 2) = 2 \, z_2(\tau_1) - 1.$$

These equations tell us how to transform α to obtain the curve β where u_1 changes sign. Starting at the origin with $\eta_1 + \eta_2 < 0$ and $\eta_1 + 2\eta_2 \geqq 0$, we have $u_1 = -1$ and $u_2 = 1$ and u_1 must change sign some time not later than $\tau = \ln 2$ and can do so at any point along the line from $(0, 0)$ to $(-1, 0)$. This is the switching curve γ. The other switching curves α', β', γ' are obtained by symmetry. It is clear that these are the only possible switching curves, and this gives a control law for the complete state space.

EXAMPLE 17.4. Let us consider the optimal control problem of coming to the origin in minimum time for

$$\dot{x}_1 = -x_1 + u_1,$$
$$\dot{x}_2 = -2x_2 + u_1 + u_2, \qquad |u_1| \leq 1, \quad |u_2| \leq 1.$$

As was shown in Example 17.1, this system is proper but not normal. Since the eigenvalues are negative, there does exist optimal control for the whole state space R^2, but it will not be uniquely determined by $u = \text{sgn}[\eta' Y(t)]$. However, it is possible to determine switching curves that give a unique optimal trajectory through each point of the state space and hence an optimal control law. Here

$$\eta' Y(t) = (\eta_1 e^t + \eta_2 e^{2t}, \eta_2 e^{2t}).$$

Letting $t = -\tau$, we examine the solutions of

$$dx_1/d\tau = x_1 - u_1,$$
$$dx_2/d\tau = 2x_2 - u_1 - u_2,$$

leaving the origin with control satisfying

$$u_1(\tau) = \text{sgn}(\eta_1 e^{-\tau} + \eta_2 e^{-2\tau}), \qquad u_2(\tau) = \text{sgn}(\eta_2 e^{-2\tau}).$$

All such solutions give optimal trajectories (Corollary 17.2). Taking $\eta_2 = 0$, we can choose u_2 to be any value between -1 and 1 and switch values any time we please. We restrict ourselves to values -1, 0, or 1.

The curve α in Fig. 17.3 corresponds to $\eta_1 < 0$, $\eta_2 = 0$, and $u_1 = -1$, $u_2 = 1$. If we switch to $u_2 = 0$, the trajectories leaving α are parabolas with vertices at $(-1, -\frac{1}{2})$. The curve β corresponds to switching at time $\tau = 0$, and every point between α and β has an optimal trajectory passing through it. The curve β corresponds to leaving the origin with $u_1 = -1$, $u_2 = 0$. Switching to $u_2 = -1$, we leave β at any point we please along parabolas with vertices at $(-1, -1)$. The curve γ corresponds to switching to $u_2 = -1$ at time $\tau = 0$; that is, to leaving the origin with $u_1 = -1$, $u_2 = -1$. All points between β and γ can be reached in this way. Picking $\eta_1 > 0$ and $\eta_1 + \eta_2 < 0$, we see that we can switch to $u_1 = 1$ at any point along γ we please. The trajectories leaving γ are parabolas with vertices at $(1, 0)$ and each point between γ and α' can be reached in this way. The switching curves α', β' and γ' are obtained by symmetry. There are an infinity of ways in which this could be done.

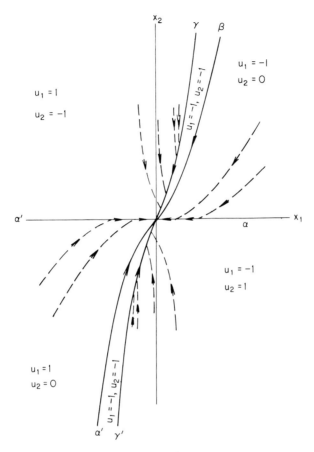

FIG. 17.3.

EXERCISE 17.5. Assume that the system (17.1) is normal. Let $-x^0$ be on the boundary of $\mathscr{R}(t^*)$ and let η be an outward normal to $\mathscr{R}(t^*)$ at $-x^0$. For any γ with the property that $\gamma' x^0 < 0$, define

$$u_\gamma(t) = \operatorname{sgn}[\gamma' Y(t)]$$

and

$$F(t, \gamma, x^0) = \gamma'[x^0 + y(t, u_\gamma)].$$

Show that $F(t, \gamma, x^0) = 0$ defines a function $T(\gamma, x^0)$ with the property that $T(\gamma, x^0) < T(\eta, x^0) = t^*$ for any γ that is not an outward normal to $\mathscr{R}(t^*)$ at x^0. The problem of computing η (and hence of computing the optimal control u to go from x^0 to the origin) is therefore reduced to that of maximizing $T(\gamma, x^0)$.

EXERCISE 17.6. Solve the problem of Example 17.2 with $|u| \leq 1$ replaced by $-a \leq u \leq b$, $a > 0$, $b > 0$. What can be said if $a = 0$ (for instance, what is the attainable set)?

18. Transversatility and a Sufficient Condition for the General Problem

For a continuously moving target $z(t)$ we know that a necessary condition for u^* to be an optimal control is that u^* be of the form

$$u^*(t) = \operatorname{sgn}[\eta' Y(t)] \tag{18.1}$$

for some $\eta \neq 0$; that is, along an optimal trajectory, optimal control maximizes $\eta' \dot{y}(t, u)$ and therefore maximizes $\eta' X^{-1}(t) \dot{x}(t, u)$. This, as was pointed out in Section 13, is a special case of Pontryagin's maximum principle.

It is easy to see that this necessary condition applies also when $z(t)$ is replaced by any continuously moving compact target set $S(t)$ [$S(t)$ is a continuous function on $[0, \infty)$ to the metric space of compact subsets of R^n] or by any stationary target set S in R^n. Just as before one can show that if t^* is the minimum time and $p \in \mathscr{A}(t^*) \cap S(t^*)$, then p must be on the boundary of both $\mathscr{A}(t^*)$ and $S(t^*)$. If S is a fixed target set and a point p of S is reached in minimum time, then the control to reach p is optimal and p must be on the boundary of both S and $\mathscr{A}(t^*)$.

We now want to obtain further necessary conditions, called transversality conditions, which tell how an optimal trajectory behaves as it approaches the target and how the target behaves as it approaches the attainable set $\mathscr{A}(t^*)$.

Consider first the case of a moving point target $z(t)$ and assume that $z(t)$ is continuously differentiable and that $A(t)$ and $B(t)$ are continuous. In the y space the moving target is

$$w(t) = X^{-1}(t) z(t) - x^0.$$

Let u^* be an optimal control to hit $z(t)$ and let t^* be the minimum time. Then $w(t^*) = y(t^*; u^*)$ and $w(t) \notin \mathcal{R}(t)$ for $t \in [0, t^*)$. Thus by Theorem 9.1 there is for each $t \in [0, t^*)$ a support plane $\pi(t)$ to $\mathcal{R}(t)$ at a point $q(t)$ of the boundary of $\mathcal{R}(t)$ which separates $w(t)$ and $R(t)$. Let $\eta(t)$ be a unit normal to $\pi(t)$ outward relative to $\mathcal{R}(t)$. It then follows that

$$\eta'(t)[q(t) - y(t, u^*)] \geqq 0,$$
$$\eta'(t)[w(t) - q(t)] \geqq 0,$$

and

$$\eta'(t)[w(t) - y(t, u^*)] \geqq 0 \qquad \text{for all} \quad t \in [0, t^*).$$

By compactness of the unit sphere in R^n and compactness of $\mathcal{R}(t^*)$ we can select a sequence of times $t_k \in [0, t^*)$ such that $t_k \to t^*$, $\eta(t_k) \to \eta$, and $q(t_k) \to q$ as $k \to \infty$. Since $\eta'(t)[w(t) - q(t)] = |w(t) - q(t)|$, the distance of $w(t)$ from $\mathcal{R}(t)$, it follows that $q = w(t^*)$. Let p be any point in $\mathcal{R}(t^*)$. Then for some admissible control u, $p = y(t^*, u)$ and $\eta'(t_k)[q(t_k) - y(t_k, u)] \geqq 0$. Letting $k \to \infty$ we can conclude that η is an outward normal to $\mathcal{R}(t^*)$ at $q = w(t^*) = y(t^*, u)$. Hence

$$\eta'(t_k) \frac{y(t_k, u^*) - w(t_k)}{t_k - t^*}$$

$$= \eta'(t_k) \left\{ \frac{[y(t_k, u^*) - y(t^*, u^*)]}{t_k - t^*} + \frac{[w(t^*) - w(t_k)]}{t_k - t^*} \right\} \geqq 0. \tag{18.2}$$

Since $\eta' Y(t)u^*(t)$ is continuous and $|\int_{t_k}^{t^*} Y(\tau) u(\tau) \, d\tau| < K|t^* - t_k|$ for some constant K, it follows that $\eta'y(t, u^*)$ is differentiable and

$$\frac{d}{dt} \eta' y(t, u^*) = \eta' Y(t) u^*(t).$$

Letting $k \to \infty$ in Eq. (18.2), we obtain

$$\eta'\dot{w}(t^*) \leqq \eta' Y(t^*) u^*(t^*) = \eta'\dot{y}(t^*, u^*). \tag{18.3}$$

Rewriting this inequality yields the following necessary condition for optimal control to a continuously moving target:

Theorem 18.1 Assume that $A(t)$, $B(t)$, and $\dot{z}(t)$ are continuous and let u^* be an optimal control to hit $z(t)$ with t^* the minimum time. Then for some $\eta \neq 0$

$$\eta' X^{-1}(t^*)\, \dot{z}(t^*) \leqq \eta' X^{-1}(t^*)[A(t^*)\, x(t^*, u^*) + B(t^*)\, u^*(t^*)], \quad (18.4)$$

where $u^*(t) = \text{sgn}[\eta' Y(t)]$.

We shall give a geometric interpretation of inequality (18.3) in terms of the target function $w(t)$ and the reachable set function $\mathscr{R}(t)$. A similar interpretation follows for inequality (18.4), $z(t)$ and $\mathscr{A}(t)$.

Lemma 13.1 showed that the condition $u^*(t) = \text{sgn}[\eta' Y(t)]$ was necessary and sufficient for $y(t^*, u^*) = w(t^*)$ to be a boundary point of $\mathscr{R}(t^*)$. This assures that the intercept, with $w(t)$, occurs on the boundary. For t^* to be optimal, we must have that as t increases to t^* the target $w(t)$ is *not* approaching the boundary of the reachable set from within this set. We shall show that this is the interpretation of inequality (18.3).

Geometrically, η is an outward normal to a support plane $\pi(t^*)$ of $\mathscr{R}(t^*)$ at $y(t^*, u^*)$. Let $h^1(\eta), \ldots, h^{n-1}(\eta)$ denote $(n-1)$ linearly independent unit vectors, each orthogonal to η, which determine $\pi(t^*)$. Then the vectors $\{(1, \dot{y}(t^*, u^*)), (0, h^1(\eta)), \ldots, (0, h^{n-1}(\eta))\}$ are n linearly independent vectors in the $(n+1)$-dimensional (t, y) space and determine a hyperplane P at the point $(t^*, y(t^*, u^*))$. A normal to P, directed (at least locally) away from the reachable cone $\{(t, y): t \geqq 0, y \in \mathscr{R}(t)\}$ is $(-\eta' \dot{y}(t^*, u^*), \eta)$. If $w(t)$ is to approach the reachable cone from outside the cone, the inner product of $(1, \dot{w}(t^*))$ with $(-\eta' \dot{y}(t^*, u^*, \eta)$ must be nonpositive. This is inequality (18.3).

If S is any stationary set in R^n and u^* is an optimal control to hit S and if it hits S in time t^* at a point p of S, then u^* is an optimal control to hit $z(t) \equiv p$. Note also in this case, since p is outside $\mathscr{A}(t)$ for $0 \leqq t < t^*$, that $w(t) = X^{-1}(t) p - x^0$ is outside $\mathscr{R}(t)$ for $0 \leqq t < t^*$. Using Theorem 18.1 we summarize the transversality for a stationary target as:

Corollary 18.1 If $A(t)$ and $B(t)$ are continuous and u^* is an optimal control to hit a stationary target S in minimum time t^*, then for some $\eta \neq 0$

$$\eta' X^{-1}(t^*)\, \dot{x}(t^*, u^*) = \eta' X^{-1}(t^*)[A(t^*)\, x(t^*, u^*) + B(t^*)\, u^*(t^*)] \geqq 0,$$

$$(18.5)$$

where $u^*(t) = \text{sgn}[\eta' Y(t)]$.

If the inequality ($\geqq 0$) in (18.4), or (18.5) for stationary targets, can be replaced by strict inequality (>0) we have strict transversality.

Strict transversality, sometimes referred to as a penetrating condition, may be used to obtain a sufficient condition for the general problem.

It was previously noted (Section 17) that $\mathscr{R}(t)$ expanding does not imply that $\mathscr{A}(t)$ will be expanding. This is easily seen from the relation $\mathscr{A}(t) = \{X(t)(x^0 + y): y \in \mathscr{R}(t)\}$. Thus, even for a stationary target z and a proper system, it is possible for z to belong to the interior of $\mathscr{A}(t_1)$ and to the boundary of $\mathscr{A}(t_2)$ for some $t_2 > t_1$. For this case, and the more general case of a continuously moving target $z(t)$, we define t^* to be a *local minimum time* and u^* a *local optimal control* if $x(t^*, u^*) = z(t^*)$ while for some $\delta > 0$, $z(t) \notin \mathscr{A}(t)$ for $t^* - \delta \leqq t < t^*$.

Theorem 18.2 Let $A(t)$ and $B(t)$ be continuous and $z(t)$ be a continuously differentiable target. Suppose u^* is an admissible control such that $x(t^*, u^*) = z(t^*)$. A sufficient condition that u^* be a local optimal control and t^* a local minimum time is that u^* satisfy the necessary condition $u^*(t) = \mathrm{sgn}[\eta' Y(t)]$ for some $\eta \neq 0$ and the strict transversality condition

$$\eta' X^{-1}(t^*)\, \dot{z}(t^*) < \eta' X^{-1}(t^*)\, \dot{x}(t^*, u^*). \tag{18.6}$$

Proof. The transversality condition (18.6) is equivalent to

$$\eta' \dot{w}(t^*) < \eta' \dot{y}(t^*, u^*)$$

in the y space. Since $\dot{w}$ and $\dot{y}$ are continuous there exists a $\delta > 0$ such that for $t \in [t^* - \delta, t^*)$

$$\int_t^{t^*} \eta' \dot{w}(\tau)\, d\tau < \int_t^{t^*} \eta' \dot{y}(\tau, u^*)\, d\tau$$

or, using the fact that $w(t^*) = y(t^*, u^*)$,

$$\eta' y(t, u^*) < \eta' w(t), \quad t \in [t^* - \delta, t^*). \tag{18.7}$$

From Corollary 13.1, in particular Eq. (13.5), we see that $u^*(t) = \mathrm{sgn}[\eta' Y(t)]$ implies $\eta' y(t, u) \leqq \eta' y(t, u^*)$ for all $t \geqq 0$ and any admissible control u. Combining this with (18.7) gives

$$\eta' y(t, u) < \eta' w(t), \quad t \in [t^* - \delta, t^*). \tag{18.8}$$

Now suppose t^* is not a local minimum time. Then $w(t) \in \mathscr{R}(t)$ for some $t_1 \in [t^* - \delta, t^*)$, and hence there is a control u such that $y(t_1, u) = w(t_1)$. This contradicts (18.8), completing the proof.

It is interesting to note that any conditions which yield $\eta' X^{-1}(t^*) \dot{x}(t^*, u^*) > 0$ in (18.5) of Corollary 18.1 with S a stationary point target p will, by Theorem 18.2, be sufficient conditions for t^* to be a local minimum time. In particular, if p is the origin and u^* satisfies the necessary condition $u^*(t) = \text{sgn}[\eta' Y(t)]$,

$$\eta' X^{-1}(t^*) \dot{x}(t^*, u^*) = \eta' Y(t^*)u^*(t^*) = \sum_{j=1}^{n} |(\eta' Y(t^*))_j|.$$

In this case one might expect strict transversality for a proper system. However our next example will show that even for a normal system this need not be the case.

EXAMPLE 18.1. Consider, again, the normal system $\ddot{x} + x = u$, $|u| \leq 1$, of Example 17.2. Our problem will be to reach the origin in minimum time from the initial point $(2, 0)$.

As we saw in Examples 13.1 and 17.2, if we choose an arbitrary η' of the form $(\cos \delta, \sin \delta)$ then a necessary condition that a control be optimal is that it have the form $\text{sgn}[\sin(t + \delta)]$. For our problem if we choose $\delta = 0$, $\eta' = (1, 0)$, $u^*(t) = 1$ for $0 \leq t \leq \pi$ and $x_1(t, u^*) = 1 + \cos t$, $x_2(t, u^*) = -\sin t$. Thus $x(0, u^*) = (2, 0)$, $x(\pi, u^*) = (0, 0)$, while u^* satisfies the required necessary condition. However $\eta' X^{-1}(t) \dot{x}(t, u^*) \equiv 0$, $0 \leq t \leq \pi$. On the other hand, Corollary 17.2 shows that $u^* \equiv 1$ is optimal and π is the minimum time. This shows that strict transversality even for a normal autonomous system and stationary target is not a necessary condition for optimality.

EXERCISE 18.1. In Theorem 18.1 let the target be a continuously moving compact convex target set $S(t)$. Show that there is an $\eta \neq 0$ such that at the point $x(t^*, u^*)$ the hyperplane normal to η is a support plane to $S(t^*)$ with η an inner normal and $u^*(t) = \text{sgn}[\eta' Y(t)]$ (see Exercise 9.3).

EXERCISE 18.2. Establish the result in Exercise 18.1 under the assumption that the target S is a stationary closed convex set.

EXERCISE 18.3. Determine the switching curves to hit the sphere $S = \{x: |x| = \varepsilon\}$ in minimum time for:

(a) $\ddot{x} = u$, $|u| \leqq 1$;
(b) $\ddot{x} + x = u$, $|u| \leqq 1$;
(c) $\ddot{x} + x = u$, $-a \leqq u \leqq b$, $a > 0$, $b > 0$.

EXERCISE 18.4. In Exercise 18.3b, choose an $\varepsilon > 0$ and, for x^0 in a neighborhood of $(2 + \varepsilon, 0)$, compute the optimal time $t^*(x^0)$. Show that t^* is not a differentiable function.

19. Controllability with Unlimited Control

We consider the same fundamental system

$$\dot{x} = A(t)\,x + B(t)\,u(t)), \qquad x(t_0) = x^0, \tag{19.1}$$

but wish now to remove the constraint $|u_i(t)| \leqq 1$, $i = 1, \ldots, r$. Instead we consider throughout this section a more general class Ω^* of admissible controls and shall only require them to be square summable on finite intervals. Assume also that $A(t)$ and $B(t)$ are matrix-valued functions defined on $[0, \infty)$ and that they are square summable on finite intervals.

We now define the various controllability concepts that we wish to discuss in this section. The system (19.1) is said to be *controllable on an interval* $[t_0, t_1]$ if, given x^0 and x^1 in R^n, there is a control $u \in \Omega^*$ which brings the system (19.1) starting at time t_0 at x^0 to x^1 at time t_1; that is, there is an admissible control that transfers the system from (t_0, x^0) to (t_1, x^1). If the system (19.1) is controllable on $[t_0, t_1]$ for some $t_1 > t_0$ we say that the system (19.1) is *controllable at time* t_0. If the system (19.1) is controllable at each $t_0 \geqq 0$, we say simply that it is *controllable*. The adjective "completely" is sometimes used with these two concepts of controllability but seems unnecessary and it is convenient to drop it. We say that the system is *fully controllable at time* t_0 if it is controllable on $[t_0, t_1]$ for each $t_1 > t_0$, that is, one can start at

x^0 at time t_0 and by admissible control reach any point x^1 in an arbitrarily short time (any time $t_1 > t_0$). If the system is fully controllable at each $t_0 \geq 0$ we again say simply that the system is *fully controllable*. It is clear that full controllability implies controllability, and as we will see in this section *full controllability is equivalent to a system being proper*. The principal objective of this section is to obtain sufficient conditions for controllability that are useful and can be checked without solving the differential equations for the system.

Since the constraint $|u_i| \leq 1$, $i = 1, \ldots, r$, has been removed, the control

$$u(t) = Y'(t)\xi, \quad \xi \in R^n, \tag{19.2}$$

is admissible ($u \in \Omega^*$) and for this control

$$x(t) = X(t)\, X^{-1}(t_0)\, x^0 + X(t) \int_{t_0}^t Y(\tau)\, Y'(\tau)\, \xi\, d\tau$$

$$= X(t)\, X^{-1}(t_0)\, x^0 + X(t)\, M(t, t_0)\, \xi, \tag{19.3}$$

where

$$M(t_0, t) = \int_{t_0}^t Y(\tau)\, Y'(\tau)\, d\tau. \tag{19.4}$$

Hence if $M(t_0, t_1)$ is nonsingular and we want $x(t_1) = x^1$ we can solve (19.3) for ξ and obtain

$$\xi = M^{-1}(t_0, t_1)[X^{-1}(t_1)\, x^1 - X^{-1}(t_0)\, x^0]. \tag{19.5}$$

Equations (19.5) and (19.2) give us an explicit expression for a control that transfers the system from (t_0, x^0) to (t_1, x^1). This leads us to a relationship between $M(t_0, t_1)$ and controllability

Theorem 19.1   The following are equivalent:
  A. $M(t_0, t_1)$ is nonsingular;
  B. the system (19.1) is controllable on $[t_0, t_1]$;
  C. the system (19.1) is proper on $[t_0, t_1]$.

Proof. It is clear that $M(t_0, t_1)$ nonsingular is equivalent to $M(t_0, t_1)$ is positive definite, and this in turn is equivalent to $\eta' Y(t) \equiv 0$ a.e. on $[t_0, t_1]$ implies $\eta = 0$. Therefore A and C are equivalent. We show next that if the system is not proper on $[t_0, t_1]$, then it is not controllable.

If it is not proper on $[t_0, t_1]$, then there is an $\eta \neq 0$ for which $\eta' Y(t) \equiv 0$ a.e. on $[t_0, t_1]$ and for any admissible control u:

$$\eta' X^{-1}(t_1)\, x(t_1) - \eta' X^{-1}(t_0) = \eta' \int_{t_0}^{t_1} Y(t)\, u(t)\, dt = 0.$$

Let c be the constant vector $\eta' X^{-1}(t_0)$. Then the only points x^1 that can be attained in time t_1 lie on the plane $\eta' X^{-1}(t_1) x^1 = c$. This proves that C implies B. We have already shown above that A implies B, and the proof is complete.

We then have immediately:

Corollary 19.1 The following are equivalent:
  A. $M(t_0, t_1)$ is nonsingular for some $t_1 > t_0$;
  B. the system (19.1) is controllable at t_0;
  C. the system (19.1) is proper on $[t_0, t_1]$ for some $t_1 > t_0$.

Corollary 19.2 The following are equivalent:
  A. $M(t_0, t_1)$ is nonsingular for all $t_1 > t_0$;
  B. the system is fully controllable at time t_0;
  C. the system is proper at time t_0.

Corollary 19.3 The following are equivalent:
  A. $M(t_0, t_1)$ is nonsingular for all $t_1 > t_0$ and all $t_0 \geq 0$;
  B. system (19.1) is fully controllable;
  C. system (19.1) is proper.

EXERCISE 19.1. Prove the equivalence of B and C in Theorem 19.1 using Theorem 17.5.

EXERCISE 19.2. Assuming that the system is controllable on $[t_0, t_1]$ show that the control defined by (19.2) and (19.5) is the "minimum energy control" to transfer the system from (t_0, x^0) to (t_1, x^1), where the control energy $E(u)$ is defined by $E(u) = \int_{t_0}^{t_1} |u(t)|^2\, dt$.

EXERCISE 19.3. Generalize Exercise 19.2 with the control energy defined by $E(u) = \int_{t_0}^{t_1} u'(t)\, Q(t)\, u(t)\, dt$, where $Q(t)$ is a positive definite $r \times r$ matrix.

The necessary and sufficient condition given in terms of $M(t_0, t_1)$ in Corollary 19.3, while of theoretical interest, is usually not very useful. To apply this criterion one must know $Y(t) = X^{-1}(t) B(t)$, and this means that one must know the principle matrix solution $X(t)$ of $\dot{x} = A(t) x$. Hence applying this criteria can be extremely difficult even when A is a constant matrix and almost impossible when A depends upon time. What we want to do now is to obtain conditions for controllability that depend directly upon the matrices $A(t)$ and $B(t)$ and are therefore directly computable. We have already done this when A and B are constant matrices and know that the autonomous system $\dot{x} = Ax + Bu$ is proper if and only if

$$\text{rank}[B, AB, \ldots, A^{n-1}B] = n. \tag{19.6}$$

What we want to do now is to generalize this condition under the assumption that the matrix $Y(t)$ has continuous derivatives. We will assume that $A(t)$ has $k - 2$ continuous derivatives and that $B(t)$ has $k - 1$ continuous derivatives. This means that $Y(t)$ has $k - 1$ continuous derivatives.

We obtain first a necessary and sufficient condition for controllability at time t_0 and then later will obtain some sufficient conditions that are often easier to apply (see Section 17 for the definition of Γ).

Theorem 19.2 Assume that A has $(n - 2)$ continuous derivatives and that B has $(n - 1)$ continuous derivatives on $[t_0, \infty)$. The system (19.1) is controllable at t_0 if and only if there exist times $t_1, \ldots, t_n \geq t_0$ (all greater than or equal to t_0) for which

$$\text{rank}[X^{-1}(t_1) B(t_1), X^{-1}(t_2) \Gamma B(t_2), \ldots, X^{-1}(t_n) \Gamma^{n-1} B(t_n)] = n. \tag{19.7}$$

Proof. From (17.5) we see the condition (19.7) is equivalent to

$$\text{rank}[Y(t_1), DY(t_2), \ldots, D^{n-1}Y(t_n)] = n. \tag{19.8}$$

To prove sufficiency of this condition we will show that (19.1) not controllable at t_0 implies that $\text{rank}[Y(t_1), \ldots, D^{n-1}Y(t_n)] < n$ for any set $t_1, \ldots, t_n \geq t_0$. Indeed (19.1) not controllable at t_0 implies [since $Y(t)$ is continuous] that there exists a nonzero vector η such that $\eta' Y(t) = 0$ for all $t \geq t_0$ (Corollary 19.1). This implies $\eta' DY(t), \ldots, \eta' D^{n-1}(t) Y(t)$ are also zero for all $t \geq t_0$. Therefore, for any set $t_1, \ldots, t_n \geq t_0$, $\text{rank}[(t_1), \ldots, D^{n-1}Y(t_n)] < n$.

In order to show necessity of the condition we assume that the system (19.1) is controllable at t_0. We will then establish the existence of times $t_1, t_2, \ldots, t_n \geq t_0$ for which (19.8) is satisfied that is, for any nonzero vector η that the nr-dimensional vector $[Y(t)$ is an $n \times r$ matrix$]$ $\eta'[Y(t_1), DY(t_2), \ldots, D^{n-1}Y(t_n)] \neq 0$. Let e^1 be any nonzero vector. Since (19.1) is controllable and therefore proper at t_0, there is a $t_1 > t_0$ such that $e^{1'}Y(t_1) \neq 0$. If rank$[Y(t_1)] = n$, we are finished. If not, there is a unit vector e^2 such that $e^{2'}Y(t_1) = 0$, and clearly e^1 and e^2 are linearly independent.

We next show that there exists a $t_2 \geq t_0$ such that $e^{2'}DY(t_2) \neq 0$. Indeed, suppose $e^{2'}DY(t) = 0$ for all $t \geq t_0$. Then

$$0 = \int_{t_1}^{t} e^{2'}DY(\tau)\,d\tau = e^{2'}Y(t)$$

for all $t \geq t_0$, which contradicts the controllability of (19.1) at t_0 (Corollary 19.1). We continue inductively in this manner and either for some $j < n$,

$$\text{rank}[Y(t_1), DY(t_2), \ldots, D^{j-1}Y(t_j)] = n,$$

and we are finished or else we generate n linearly independent vectors $e^1, e^2, \ldots, e^n$ and times $t_1, t_2, \ldots, t_n \geq t_0$ for which

$$e^{k'}[Y(t_1), DY(t_2), \ldots, D^{k-2}Y(t_{k-1})] = 0, \quad k = 2, \ldots, n, \qquad (19.9)$$

and

$$e^k D^{k-1} Y(t_k) \neq 0, \quad k = 1, \ldots, n. \qquad (19.10)$$

Now any nonzero vector η can be expressed as $\eta = \sum_{i=1}^{n} \alpha_i e^i$, not all $\alpha_i = 0$. Then

$$\eta'[Y(t_1), DY(t_2), \ldots, D^{n-1}Y(t_n)]$$

$$= \left[\alpha_1 e^1 Y(t_1), \sum_{i=1}^{2} \alpha_i e^{i'}DY(t_2), \ldots, \sum_{i=1}^{n} \alpha_i e^{i'}D^{n-1}Y(t_n)\right],$$

and it is clear from (19.10) that this nr-dimensional vector cannot be zero since all of the α_i's are not zero. This completes the proof.

In much the same way as was used to obtain the sufficiency of the above condition we obtain:

Theorem 19.3 If $A(t)$ has $k - 2$ continuous derivatives and $B(t)$ has $k - 1$ continuous derivatives, then the system (19.1) is fully controllable (proper) at t_0 if for some positive integer k

(a) $$\text{rank}[B(t_0), \Gamma B(t_0), \ldots, \Gamma^{k-1} B(t_0)] = n$$

or, more generally,
(b) for each $t_1 > t_0$ there is a $t \in [t_0, t_1)$ for which

$$\text{rank}[B(t), \Gamma B(t), \ldots, \Gamma^{k-1} B(t)] = n.$$

Proof. Assume that (19.1) is not proper at $t_0 \geq 0$. Since $Y(t)$ is continuous, this implies that $\eta' Y(t) \equiv 0$ on $[t_0, t_1]$ for some $\eta \neq 0$ and some $t_1 > t_0$. Differentiating $\eta' Y(t) = \eta' X^{-1}(t) B(t)$, we obtain

$$\eta' X^{-1}(t) B(t) = 0, \; \eta' X^{-1}(t) \Gamma(t) B(t)$$
$$= 0, \ldots, \eta' X^{-1}(t) \Gamma^{k-1}(t) B(t) = 0$$

for $t \in [t_0, t_1]$. Therefore the nonzero vector $\eta' X^{-1}(t)$ is in the null space of each of the matrices $B(t), \Gamma B(t), \ldots, \Gamma^{k-1} B(t)$ and

$$\text{rank}[B(t), \Gamma B(t), \ldots, \Gamma^{k-1} B(t)] < n \qquad \text{for all} \quad t \in [t_0, t_1].$$

This contradicts both (a) and (b) and completes the proof.

The following example illustrates a case where it would not be possible to decide controllability using $M(t_0, t_1)$:

EXAMPLE 19.1.

$$\dot{x} = A(t) x + B(t) u,$$

where $n = 2$,

$$B(t) = \begin{pmatrix} t^2 \\ t^3 \end{pmatrix},$$

and $A(0) = DA(0) = D^2 A(0) = 0$. Under these conditions $\Gamma^j B(0) = D^j B(0)$ for $j = 0, 1, 2, 3$. Therefore

$$B(0) = \Gamma B(0) = \begin{pmatrix} 0 \\ 0 \end{pmatrix}, \qquad \Gamma^2 B(0) = \begin{pmatrix} 2 \\ 0 \end{pmatrix}, \qquad \Gamma^3 B(0) = \begin{pmatrix} 0 \\ 6 \end{pmatrix}$$

Since $\Gamma^2 B(0)$ and $\Gamma^3 B(0)$ are linearly independent, it follows from Theorem 19.3 that the system is fully controllable (proper) at $t_0 = 0$.

EXERCISE 19.4. Show that

$$\dot{x}_1 = t^4 u_1(t),$$
$$\dot{x}_2 = t^3 u_2(t)$$

is fully controllable (proper) at $t_0 = 0$ using (a) Corollary 19.1 and (b) Theorem 19.3. Is this system proper (fully controllable)?

Theorem 19.2 certainly suggests that the conditions in Theorem 19.3, while sufficient, may not be necessary. We will illustrate now that this is so even when A and B are C^∞ (to say that A and B are C^∞ means that all the derivatives of A and B exist and are therefore continuous).

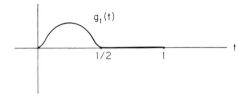

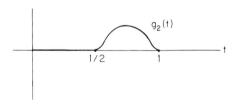

FIG. 19.1.

Let g_1 and g_2 be periodic of period 1 and on the interval $[0, 1]$ and be as shown in Fig. 19.1. These functions can be made to approach zero like e^{-1/t^2} and can be made C^∞. Define

$$b_1(t) = e^{-1/t^2} g_1\left(\frac{1}{t}\right), \qquad \text{for} \quad t > 0, \quad b_1(0) = 0,$$

$$b_2(t) = e^{-1/t^2} g_2\left(\frac{1}{t}\right), \qquad \text{for} \quad t > 0, \quad b_2(0) = 0.$$

Since $\int_0^{t_1} b_i(t)\,dt > 0$ for $i = 1, 2$ and all $t_1 > 0$, the system

$$\dot{x}_1 = b_1(t)\,u_1(t),$$
$$\dot{x}_2 = b_2(t)\,u_2(t) \qquad\qquad (19.11)$$

is proper (fully controllable) at $t_0 = 0$. This follows since $\mathcal{R}(t_1, 0)$ contains the origin in its interior for each $t_1 > 0$ (Corollary 17.3). It is also easy to see, since either $g_1(t) \equiv 0$ or $g_2(t) \equiv 0$ on $[t_0, t_0 + \delta]$ for each $t_0 > 0$ and sufficiently small $\delta > 0$, that the system is not proper at any $t_0 > 0$. Now

$$\text{rank}[b(0), \Gamma b(0), \ldots, \Gamma^{k-1} b(0)] = 0$$

and

$$\text{rank}[b(t), \Gamma b(t), \ldots, \Gamma^{k-1} b(t)] \leq 1$$

for all $t \geq 0$ and all integers $k = 1, 2, \ldots$. Thus even for C^∞ functions and k arbitrarily large the conditions of Theorem 19.3 are not necessary. This is similar to the fact that the vanishing of the Wronskian is a sufficient but not necessary condition for functions to be linearly independent.

What we want to do now is show, under the assumption that $A(t)$ and $B(t)$ are analytic or piecewise analytic on $[0, \infty)$, that a condition similar to (b) in Theorem 19.3 is both necessary and sufficient for a system to be proper (fully controllable) at t_0. By piecewise analytic we mean piecewise continuous with only isolated singularities (points where the function is not analytic). For instance, the functions $b_1(t)$ and $b_2(t)$ of Eq. (19.11) (Fig. 19.1) can be made piecewise analytic. The system given by Eq. (19.11) is really pathological, and for most practical purposes the results we will now obtain gives us a necessary and sufficient condition that a system be proper (fully controllable).

Let (t_0, t_1) be a fixed nonempty open interval and define

$$\mu(k, t_0, t_1) = \max_{t \in (t_0, t_1)} \text{rank}[B(t), \Gamma B(t), \ldots, \Gamma^{k-1} B(t)].$$

Then $\mu(k, t_0, t_1)$ is defined when $B(t)$ and $A(t)$ have enough derivatives on (t_0, t_1) so that $\Gamma^{k-1}(t)\, B(t)$ is defined on (t_0, t_1). Assume now that $\mu(m, t_0, t_1)$ is defined for some integer $m > n$. Since $\mu(k, t_0, t_1) \leq n$, there is at least one integer $n^* \leq n$ such that $\mu(n^*, t_0, t_1) = \mu(n^* + 1, t_0, t_1)$. Let $n_0 = \mu(n^*, t_0, t_1)$ and let $\beta^1(t), \ldots, \beta^{n_0}(t)$ be n_0 column vectors from $[B(t), \ldots, \Gamma^{n^*-1}(t) B(t)]$ which are linearly independent at $t^* \in (t_0, t_1)$. By Exercise 19.6 these vectors are linearly independent for $t \in (t_0^*, t_1^*)$, some nonempty subinterval of (t_0, t_1). Let $\beta^{n_0+1}(t)$ be a column vector of $\Gamma^{n^*}(t) B(t)$. Then, since $\mu(n^*, t_0, t_1) = \mu(n^* + 1, t_0, t_1)$, $\beta^{n_0+1}(t) = c_1(t) \beta^1(t) + \cdots + c_{n_0}^t \beta^{n_0}(t)$, and it follows (see Exercise 19.7) because of the nature of Γ that $\Gamma\beta^{n_0+1}(t), \beta^1(t), \ldots, \beta^{n_0}(t)$ are linearly dependent for $t \in (t_0^*, t_1^*)$. Certainly $\Gamma\beta^{n_0+1}(t), \Gamma\beta^1(t), \ldots, \Gamma\beta^{n_0}(t)$ are linearly dependent and by assumption $\Gamma\beta^i(t), \beta^1, \ldots, \beta^{n_0}$ are linearly dependent for $i = 1, 2, \ldots, n_0$. Hence the conclusion. Therefore $\mu(n^*, t_0^*, t_1^*) = \mu(n^* + 1, t_0^*, t_1^*), \ldots = \mu(m, t_0^*, t_1^*)$, and we have proved:

Lemma 19.1   If $\mu(k, t_0, t_1)$ is defined for $k = 1, 2, \ldots, m, m > n$, then for some nonempty open interval (t_0^*, t_1^*) in (t_0, t_1) and some $n^* \leq n$

$$\mu(n^*, t_0^*, t_1^*) = \mu(n^* + j, t_0^*, t_1^*)$$

for all $j = 1, \ldots, m - n^*$.

Assume now that $A(t)$ and $B(t)$ are analytic on (t_0, t_1) and that $\mu(n, t_0, t_1) < n$. Then by Lemma 19.1 there exists a (t_0^*, t_1^*) such that $\mu(k, t_0^*, t_1^*) < n$ for all integers $k = 1, 2, \ldots$. This implies that there is a $t^* \in (t_0, t_1)$ and a nonzero vector η^* for which $\eta^{*\prime}\Gamma^j B(t^*) = 0$ for all $j = 0, 1, 2, \ldots$. Taking $\eta = X(t^*) \eta^*$, we have $D^j\eta' Y(t) = 0$ at $t = t^*$ for all $j = 0, 1, 2, \ldots$. Since $\eta' Y(t)$ is analytic on (t_0, t_1), $\eta' Y(t) \equiv 0$ on (t_0, t_1). Therefore (19.1) proper at t_0 implies that $\mu(n, t_0, t_1) = n$ for all $t_1 > t_0$. Combined with Theorem 19.3 we have:

Theorem 19.4   If $A(t)$ and $B(t)$ are analytic on (t_0, t_1), $t_1 > t_0 \geq 0$ then the system (19.1) is proper (fully controllable) at t_0 if and only if for each $t_1 > t_0$ there is a $t \in (t_0, t_1)$ such that

$$\text{rank}[B(t), \Gamma(t) B(t), \ldots, \Gamma^{n-1}B(t)] = n. \tag{19.12}$$

We can, for example, apply this theorem to the system (19.11). It is piecewise analytic for $t > 0$ and we can therefore conclude that it is not proper for any $t_0 > 0$, although it is proper at $t_0 = 0$. *This is then an example of a system which is controllable for all $t_0 \geq 0$ but not proper (fully controllable) at any $t_0 > 0$.* To apply this result it is useful to note that because of analyticity Eq. (19.12) will be satisfied at all but isolated points of $[t_0, t_1]$ if the system is proper and if not proper will not be satisfied at any point of $[t_0, t_1)$.

EXERCISE 19.5. If $\xi^1, \ldots, \xi^k$ are linearly independent vectors in R^n, then, for some $\delta > 0$, $\xi^1 + v, \ldots, \xi^k + v$ are linearly independent for all v satisfying $|v| < \delta$.

EXERCISE 19.6. If $\xi^1(t), \ldots, \xi^k(t)$ are continuous and linearly independent at t_0, then there is an $\varepsilon > 0$ sucn that $\xi^1(t), \ldots, \xi^k(t)$ are linearly independent for $|t - t_0| < \varepsilon$.

EXERCISE 19.7. If $\xi^1(t), \ldots, \xi^k(t)$ are linearly independent and $\xi^{k+1}(t) = c_1(t) \xi^1(t) + \cdots + c_k(t) \xi^k(t)$ for $|t - t_0| < \varepsilon$ show that if $\xi^j(t), j = 1, \ldots, k$, are C^m for $|t - t_0| < \varepsilon$, then $c_j(t), j = 1, \ldots, k$, are also C^m for $|t - t_0| < \varepsilon$.

EXERCISE 19.8. Using the notation of Lemma 19.1, show that if

$$\text{rank}[B(t), \Gamma(t), \ldots, \Gamma^{n^*-1}(t) B(t))] = \mu(n^*, t_0, t_1),$$

for all $t \in (t_0, t_1)$, then in using condition (b) of Theorem 19.3 it is not necessary to go beyond $k = n^*$ which is less than or equal to n. In general, is it necessary or not to go beyond $k = n$?

EXERCISE 19.9. Consider the nth-order, controlled, linear differential equation

$$x^{(n)}(t) + a_{n-1}(t) x^{(n-1)}(t) + \cdots + a_0(t) x(t) = u(t),$$

where $a_j(t)$ has j continuous derivatives on $[0, \infty)$. Show that the equivalent system $\dot{y}(t) = A(t) y(t) + b(t) u(t)$, where

$$A(t) = \begin{bmatrix} 0 & 1 & 0 & . & . & . & 0 \\ 0 & 0 & 1 & . & . & . & 0 \\ . & . & . & . & . & . & . \\ . & . & . & . & . & . & . \\ . & . & . & . & . & . & 1 \\ 0 & . & . & . & 0 & . & 1 \\ -a_0 & -a_1 & . & . & . & . & -a_{n-1} \end{bmatrix}, \quad B(t) = \begin{bmatrix} 0 \\ . \\ . \\ . \\ . \\ 0 \\ 1 \end{bmatrix},$$

is fully controllable (proper) at any $t_0 \geq 0$.

EXERCISE 19.10. Let

$$A = \begin{pmatrix} 0 & -1 \\ 1 & 0 \end{pmatrix}, \qquad b(t) = \begin{pmatrix} \cos t \\ \sin t \end{pmatrix}.$$

Show that the system $\dot{x}(t) = A\,x(t) + b(t)\,u(t)$ is not controllable at $t_0 = 0$. Show that all solutions which satisfy $x(0) = 0$ lie on the surface $x_1 \sin t - x_2 \cos t = 0$ therefore there cannot be a single time $t_1 > 0$ in which all points can be reached. However, show that even with control bounded by $|u(t)| \leq 1$ any point in R^n can be attained in finite time from the initial state $x(0) = 0$.

PART III

NONLINEAR
TIME OPTIMAL CONTROL

20. General Theory

We consider the problem of reaching a continuously moving target $z(t)$ by a trajectory of the control system described by the vector differential equation

$$\dot{x}(t) = f(t, x(t), u(t)), \qquad x(0) = x^0, \tag{20.1}$$

in minimum time. The vectors x and f will be always n-dimensional. An admissible control u will be a measurable r-vector-valued-function which may have values at time t in a nonempty compact set $U(t)$, with the set-valued function U continuous in the Hausdorff topology. We will assume the vector function f is continuous in all arguments, is continuously differentiable with respect to x, and that the inner product inequality

$$x' f(t, x, u) \leqq C[1 + |x|^2] \tag{20.2}$$

holds for some constant C and all t, x, and $u \in U(t)$. This condition prevents finite escape time of trajectories and could be replaced by any condition which allows us to restrict attention to a compact set of the (t, x) space. Indeed, for any solution x of (20.1) we obtain $x'\dot{x} \leqq C[1 + |x|^2]$, $d/dt|x|^2 \leqq C[1 + |x|^2]$, or $|x(t)|^2 \leqq (1 + |x^0|^2) \exp 2Ct$. Therefore once a value $T \geqq 0$ is chosen, we need consider only the compact region

$$D(t) = \{(t, x): \quad 0 \leqq t \leqq T, |x|^2 \leqq (1 + |x^0|^2) \exp 2CT\} \tag{20.3}$$

of the $(n + 1)$-dimensional t, x space.

We next introduce the set-valued function

$$R(t, x) = \{f(t, x, u): u \in U(t)\}.$$

Since f is continuous and $U(t)$ is nonempty and compact, $R(t, x)$ is nonempty and compact. Furthermore R is continuous in the Hausdorff topology as a function of t and x. Associated with Eq. (20.1) is the equation

$$\dot{x}(t) \in R(t, x(t)), \qquad x(0) = x^0. \tag{20.4}$$

105

A solution of (20.4) is defined to be an absolutely continuous function φ such that $\varphi(0) = x^0$ and $\dot{\varphi}(t) \in R(t, \varphi(t))$ almost everywhere. The set-valued function R is introduced as a convenience in notation and presentation.

Lemma 20.1 A function φ is a solution of (20.4) if and only if φ is a solution of (20.1) for some admissible control u.

Proof. If φ is a solution of (20.1) for control u, then $\dot{\varphi}(t) = f(t, \varphi(t), u(t)) \in R(t, \varphi(t))$ almost everywhere, showing that φ is a solution of (20.4).

Conversely, suppose φ is a solution of (20.4) on an arbitrary interval $[0, T]$. Let $V(t) = \{(t, \varphi(t), u) \in E^{n+r+1} : u \in U(t)\}$. Then V is continuous in the Hausdorff topology. Also, the values $V(t)$ are nonempty, compact sets which, by the continuity of V, are contained in some fixed compact ball (with radius possibly depending on T) for $t \in [0, T]$. Clearly $R(t, \varphi(t)) = f(V(t))$. Since φ is a solution of (20.4), $\dot{\varphi}(t)$ is a measurable function with $\dot{\varphi}(t) \in R(t, \varphi(t))$ almost everywhere. By Lemma 8.1 there is a measurable function v having values $v(t) = (t, \varphi(t), u(t)) \in V(t)$ such that $\dot{\varphi}(t) = f(v(t))$; i.e., $\dot{\varphi}(t) = f(t, \varphi(t), u(t))$, where u is measurable and has values $u(t) \in U(t)$. This shows φ is a solution of (20.1), completing the proof.

The attainable set function $\mathscr{A}$ is defined, as in the linear problem, to have values $\mathscr{A}(t)$ the set of all states x attainable by trajectories of (20.1) using all possible admissible controls. Equivalently, by Lemma 20.1, $\mathscr{A}(t)$ is the set of all points $\varphi(t)$ such that φ is a solution of (20.4). Again, the existence of an optimal control for the time optimal problem will depend on $\mathscr{A}(t)$ being closed.

EXAMPLE 20.1. Consider the two-dimensional system

$$\dot{x}_1 = (1 - x_2^2)u^2, \qquad x_1(0) = 0,$$
$$\dot{x}_2 = u, \qquad x_2(0) = 0,$$

with $|u(t)| \leq 1$. We shall first show that the point $(1, 0)$ is a limit point of $\mathscr{A}(1)$ but does not belong to $\mathscr{A}(1)$.

For each positive integer n subdivide $[0, 1]$ into $2n$ equal subintervals. Let $I_j = [j/2n, (j + 1)/2n)$, $j = 0, 1, \ldots, 2n - 1$. Define

$$u''(t) = \begin{cases} 1 & \text{if } t \in I_j \text{ with } j \text{ odd,} \\ -1 & \text{if } t \in I_j \text{ with } j \text{ even.} \end{cases}$$

Let $\varphi(t, u'')$ denote the solution corresponding to u''. Then $\varphi_2(1, u'') = 0$ for all n and as $n \to \infty$, $\varphi_2(t, u'')$ converges uniformly to zero on the interval $[0, 1]$. Thus, since $(u''(t))^2 \equiv 1$,

$$\varphi_1(1, u'') = 1 - \int_0^1 \varphi_2{}^2(\tau, u'') \, d\tau < 1$$

and as $n \to \infty$, $\varphi_1(1, u'') \to 1$. However $(1, 0) \notin \mathcal{A}(1)$ since this would require a control u such that $\varphi_2(t, u) \equiv 0$ and this can occur only if $u \equiv 0$ in which case $\varphi_1(t, u) \equiv 0$.

The construction of this example depended on the fact that $R(t, x) = \{((1 - x_2{}^2)u, u) \in E^2 : -1 \leq u \leq 1\}$ is not convex for all t, x.

EXERCISE 20.1. Consider the time optimal problem of hitting the fixed target $z = (1, 0)$ with system equations those of Example 20.1. Show that for any $t' > 1$, $(1, 0) \in \mathcal{A}(t')$, and $\inf\{t : (1, 0) \in \mathcal{A}(t)\} = 1$. Does an optimal control for this problem exist?

Theorem 20.1 (Filippov). Suppose f satisfies the state continuity conditions, inequality (20.2), and that $R(t, x)$ is convex for all t, x. Then for any $T \geq 0$, $\mathcal{A}(T)$ is compact and $\mathcal{A}$ is continuous as a function of t in the Hausdorff topology.

Proof. Since $U(t)$ is continuous on $[0, T]$ there is an N such that $|u| \leq N$ whenever $u \in U(t)$, $t \in [0, T]$. Since f is continuous let M be such that $|f(t, x, y)| \leq M$ for $(t, x) \in D(T)$, $|u| \leq N$ [see (20.3) for the definition of $D(t)$].

We shall first show the closure of $\mathcal{A}(T)$. As remarked, $x \in \mathcal{A}(T)$ implies $|x|^2 \leq (1 + |x^0|^2) \exp(2CT)$, showing $\mathcal{A}(T)$ is bounded, hence, if closed, compact. Let $x'' = \varphi''(T)$ be a sequence of points in $\mathcal{A}(T)$ converging to a point x^*, with φ'' a solution of (20.4). Then $|\dot{\varphi}''(t)| \leq M$, showing the φ'' form an equicontinuous family (each has the same Lipschitz constant M). Therefore a subsequence (we take it to be the original sequence) of the φ'' converges uniformly on $[0, T]$ to a function φ which also has Lipschitz constant M and is therefore absolutely continuous. Clearly $\varphi(0) = x^0$ and $\varphi(T) = x^*$. We will next show φ is a solution of (20.4).

Let t_0 be any point of $[0, T]$ for which $\dot{\varphi}(t_0)$ exists. We will show $\dot{\varphi}(t_0) \in R(t_0, \varphi(t_0))$.

$$\frac{\varphi(t) - \varphi(t_0)}{t - t_0} = \lim_{n \to \infty} \frac{\varphi^n(t) - \varphi^n(t_0)}{t - t_0} = \lim_{n \to \infty} \frac{1}{(t - t_0)} \int_{t_0}^{t} \dot{\varphi}^n(\tau)\, d\tau$$

$$= \lim_{n \to \infty} \int_{0}^{1} \dot{\varphi}^n(t_0 + (t - t_0)s)\, ds.$$

Let $\varepsilon > 0$ be given and $\delta > 0$ be such that

$$\left| \frac{\varphi(t) - \varphi(t_0)}{t - t_0} - \dot{\varphi}(t_0) \right| < \varepsilon$$

if $|t - t_0| < \delta$.

For almost all τ, $\dot{\varphi}^n(\tau) \in R(\tau, \varphi^n(\tau))$. But φ^n converges uniformly to φ and R is continuous in the Hausdorff topology. Therefore for $|t - t_0|$ sufficiently small (and less than δ) and n sufficiently large, $\dot{\varphi}^n(\tau)$ belongs to be a closed ε neighborhood of $R(t_0, \varphi(t_0))$ for almost all $\tau \in [t_0, t]$. Denote this neighborhood by $R^\varepsilon(t_0, \varphi(t_0))$. Then $\dot{\varphi}^n(t_0 + (t - t_0)s) \in R^\varepsilon(t_0, \varphi(t_0))$ for almost all $s \in [0, 1\}$ and, since $R^\varepsilon(t_0, \varphi(t_0))$ is convex, the mean value theorem for vector-valued functions shows

$$\int_{0}^{1} \dot{\varphi}^n(t_0 + (t - t_0)s)\, ds \in R^\varepsilon(t_0, \varphi(t_0))$$

for all n sufficiently large. Thus $(\varphi(t) - \varphi(t_0))/(t - t_0)$ belongs to $R^\varepsilon(t_0, \varphi(t_0))$, hence $\dot{\varphi}(t_0) \in R^{2\varepsilon}(t_0, \varphi(t_0))$. But ε is arbitrary and $R(t_0, \varphi(t_0))$ is closed, therefore $\dot{\varphi}(t_0) \in R(t_0, \varphi(t_0))$. This holds at any point t_0 such that $\dot{\varphi}(t_0)$ exists, i.e., for almost all t_0, showing φ is a solution of (20.3). Thus $\varphi(T) = x^* \in \mathscr{A}(T)$ and $\mathscr{A}(T)$ is closed.

To complete the proof, we need only show $\mathscr{A}$ is continuous in the Hausdorff topology on $[0, T]$. Let $t_1, t_2 \in [0, T]$ and x^1 be any point in $\mathscr{A}(t_1)$ $x^1 = \varphi(t_1)$, with φ a solution of (20.4) defined on $[0, T]$. If $x^2 = \varphi(t_2) \in \mathscr{A}(t_2)$ the bound $|f(t, x, u)| \leq M$ shows $|x^1 - x^2| \leq M\,|t_1 - t_2|$. Thus given any $\varepsilon > 0$, $\mathscr{A}(t_1)$ is contained in an ε neighborhood of $\mathscr{A}(t_2)$ if $|t_1 - t_2| < \varepsilon/M$. Similarly $\mathscr{A}(t_2)$ is contained in an ε neighborhood of $\mathscr{A}(t_1)$ if $|t_1 - t_2| < \varepsilon/M$. Thus $\mathscr{A}$ is continuous and the proof is complete.

Corollary 20.1 (Existence of a Time Optimal Control). Assume the conditions of Theorem 20.1 are satisfied and that there exists a $T \geq 0$ such that the target point $z(T) \in \mathscr{A}(T)$. Then there exists an optimal control.

Proof. Let $t^* = \inf\{t: T \geq t \geq 0, z(t) \in \mathscr{A}(t)\}$. Since there is at least one value T such that $z(T) \in \mathscr{A}(T)$ by assumption, t^* is well defined. We must show $z(t^*) \in \mathscr{A}(t^*)$.

Let $\{t_n\}$ be a sequence of times converging to t^* such that $z(t_n) \in \mathscr{A}(t_n)$. For each n let φ^n be a solution of (20.4) with $\varphi^n(t_n) = z(t_n)$. Then

$$|\varphi^n(t^*) - z(t^*)| \leq |\varphi^n(t^*) - \varphi^n(t_n)| + |z(t_n) - z(t^*)|$$

$$\leq |z(t_n) - z(t^*)| + \int_{t^*}^{t_n} M \, d\tau,$$

where M is the bound on $|f(t, x, u)|$ as in the proof of Theorem 20.1. From the continuity of z, it is clear that $\{\varphi^n(t^*)\}$ converges to $z(t^*)$ as $n \to \infty$. Since $\varphi^n(t^*) \in \mathscr{A}(t^*)$ and $\mathscr{A}(t^*)$ is closed, $z(t^*) \in \mathscr{A}(t^*)$, completing the proof.

We next will prove an approximation theorem which has as a corollary an analog of the bang-bang principle. The result will not be as sharp as in the linear case. Again $R(t, x)$ will denote the set $\{f(t, x, u): u \in U(t)\}$ with f and U satisfying the continuity conditions and condition (20.2) as stated previously. We let co R denote the nonempty compact set-valued function with values co $R(t, x)$ the convex hull of $R(t, x)$; i.e.,

$$\text{co } R(t, x) = \{\alpha f(t, x, u) + (1 - \alpha)f(t, x, v): 0 \leq \alpha \leq 1, u, v \in U(t)\}.$$

$$(20.5)$$

From this representation it is clear that solutions of the equation

$$\dot{x}(t) \in \text{co } R(t, x(t)), \qquad x(0) = x^0, \tag{20.6}$$

exist. Indeed, for u, v admissible controls and $0 \leq \alpha \leq 1$, the solution of

$$\dot{x} = \alpha f(t, x, u) + (1 - \alpha)f(t, x, v), \qquad x(0) = x^0,$$

will be a solution of (20.6).

Theorem 20.2   Let φ be any solution of (20.6) on an interval $[0, T]$. Then for any $\varepsilon > 0$ there exists a solution ψ of (20.4) such that $\max_{0 \le t \le T} |\varphi(t) - \psi(t)| < \varepsilon$.

Proof. Since $U(t)$ is continuous on $[0, T]$ there is an N such that $|u| \le N$ for $u \in U(t)$, $t \in [0, T]$. Also, f is assumed continuously differentiable with respect to x. Let K be the maximum of the absolute value of all partial derivatives $(\partial/\partial x_j)f_i(t, x, u)$ for $(t, x) \in D(T)$, $|u| \le N$.

For the moment, let v be any admissible control and $\psi(t, v)$ the corresponding solution of (20.1). Then

$$|\varphi(t) - \psi(t, v)| = \left| \int_0^t [\dot\varphi(\tau) - f(\tau, \psi(\tau, v), v(\tau))] \, d\tau \right|$$

$$\le \left| \int_0^t [\dot\varphi(\tau) - f(\tau, \varphi(\tau), v(\tau))] \, d\tau \right| + \left| \int_0^t [f(\tau, \varphi(\tau), v(\tau)) \right.$$

$$\left. - f(\tau, \psi(\tau, v), v(\tau))] \, d\tau \right|$$

$$\le \left| \int_0^t [\dot\varphi(\tau) - f(\tau, \varphi(\tau), v(\tau))] \, d\tau \right|$$

$$+ n^{1/2} K \int_0^t |\varphi(\tau) - \psi(\tau)| \, d\tau.$$

The required result will follow from an application of the Gronwall inequality to (20.7) if we can show the existence of an admisisble control v which makes

$$\left| \int_0^t [\dot\varphi(\tau) - f(\tau, \varphi(\tau), v(\tau))] \, d\tau \right|$$

arbitrarily small, uniformly for $t \in [0, T]$.

Subdivide the interval $[0, T]$ into m equal subintervals each of length T/m.

Let I_j denote the interval $(j - 1)T/m < t \le jT/m$, $j = 1, 2, \ldots, m$. Since φ is a solution of (20.6), $\dot\varphi(t) \in \mathrm{co}\, R(t, \varphi(t))$ almost everywhere. By Theorem 8.4 $\int_{I_j} \mathrm{co}\, R(t, \varphi(t)) \, dt = \int_{I_j} R(t, \varphi(t)) \, dt$, which may be interpreted that there exists a measurable function y^j, defined on I_j

with value at time t in $R(t, \varphi(t))$, such that $\int_{I_j} \dot\varphi(t)\, dt = \int_{I_j} y^i(t)\, dt$. As in the proof of Lemma 20.1, one may use Lemma 8.1 to conclude that there is an admissible control v^j defined on I_j such that $y^j(t) = f(t, \varphi(t), v^j(t))$ almost everywhere. Define v^* to be that admissible control on $[0, T]$ whose restriction to I_j is v^j, $j = 1, 2, \ldots, m$. Then

$$\int_0^{jT/m} [\dot\varphi(t) - f(t, \varphi(t), v^*(t))]\, dt = 0 \qquad \text{for} \quad j = 0, \ldots, m,$$

hence

$$\left| \int_0^t [\dot\varphi(\tau) - f(\tau, \varphi(\tau), v^*(\tau))]\, d\tau \right| \leq 2Mn^{1/2}nT/m,$$

where M is the bound on $|f(t, x, u)|$ for $(t, x) \in D(T)$, $|u| \leq N$. The number m of subintervals is arbitrary; choose it large enough so that $2Mn^{1/2}T/m < \varepsilon \exp(-n^{1/2}KT)$. Then (20.7), with v replaced by v^*, becomes

$$|\varphi(t) - \psi(t, v^*)| \leq \varepsilon \exp(-n^{1/2}Kt) + n^{1/2}K \int_0^t |\varphi(\tau) - \psi(\tau, v^*)|\, d\tau.$$

An application of the Gronwall inequality gives $|\varphi(t) - \psi(t, v^*)| \leq \varepsilon$ for $0 \leq t \leq T$, showing that ψ is the desired solution of (20.4) or (20.1), completing the proof.

Corollary 20.2 Let $\mathscr{A}(T)$ and $\mathscr{B}(T)$ denote the set of points attainable at time T by solutions of (20.4) and (20.6), respectively. Then $\mathscr{A}(T)$ is dense in $\mathscr{B}(T)$ and, since $\mathscr{B}(T)$ is closed, the closure of $\mathscr{A}(T)$ is $\mathscr{B}(T)$.

EXERCISE 20.2. Consider the linear system $\dot x = A(t)\, x + B(t)\, u$, $x(0) = x^0$, with controls u satisfying $|u(t)| \leq 1$. Use Theorem 20.2 to show that any trajectory $x(t, u)$ defined on an interval $[0, T]$ may be uniformly approximated by a trajectory $x(t, u^0)$ arising from a bang-bang control u^0. Show that even in the linear case, it is not necessarily possible to find a bang-bang control u^0 such that $x(t, u) = x(t, u^0)$ for all $0 \leq t \leq T$.

21. Nonlinear Problems with Control Appearing Linearly

We now consider the special case of Eq. (20.1) of the form

$$\dot{x}(t) = g(t, x(t)) + H(t, x(t)) u(t), \qquad x(0) = x^0. \qquad (21.1)$$

The components of $g(t, x)$ and $H(t, x)$ are assumed continuous in t and x and continuously differentiable with respect to x. Here $g(t, x)$ is an n vector while $H(t, x)$ is an $n \times r$ matrix. We shall assume either that the right side of (21.1) satisfies condition (20.2) or, as in the special case of the two-dimensional examples which will follow, that there is some condition satisfied to assure that we may restrict our attention to a compact subset of (t, x) space.

For equations of the special form (21.1), if the values a control may take at time t are constrained to a set $U(t)$, we observe that $R(t, x) = \{g(t, x) + H(t, x) u : u \in U(t)\}$ is a translation of a linear image of $U(t)$. A case of particular interest is where U consists of the vertices of the unit cube in E^r; i.e.,

$$U = \{u : |u_j| = 1, j = 1, 2, \ldots, r\}.$$

Then the convex hull of U is the unit cube. Now the linear image of the convex hull of U is the convex hull of the linear image of U. Therefore, for this U, the study of $\dot{x}(t) \in R(t, x(t))$, $x(0) = x^0$, is equivalent to the study of (21.1) with admissible controls being bang-bang controls, while the sutdy of $\dot{x}(t) \in$ co $R(t, x(t))$, $x(0) = x^0$, is equivalent to the study of (21.1) with admissible controls being mesaurable functions taking values in the unit cube. Letting Ω denote this latter set of control functions, Theorem 20.2 shows: *Given any $\varepsilon > 0$ and $T > 0$, if φ is a solution of (21.1) corresponding to the arbitrary control $u \in \Omega$, there exists a bang-bang control u^0 such that the corresponding trajectory uniformly approximates φ to within ε over the interval $[0, T]$.* Corollary (20.2) shows that the closure of the set of points attainable at time T by trajectories of (21.1) corresponding to bang-bang control is the set of points attainable at time T with controls $u \in \Omega$. It is natural to wonder whether these attainable sets are actually equal, as is the case in linear systems; i.e., is the nonequality merely a shortcoming of the method of proof? In what follows, a method for constructing solutions to a class of two-dimensional nonlinear optimal control problems will be developed. Using this method, a two-dimensional example (Example 22.7) will be given to show that equality of the attainable sets for arbitrary and bang-bang controls need *not* hold.

22. Two-Dimensional, Autonomous, Nonlinear Systems with Control Appearing Linearly

We will consider systems of the form

$$\dot{x}_1(t) = A_1(x(t)) + B_1(x(t))\, u(t),$$
$$\dot{x}_2(t) = A_2(x(t)) + B_2(x(t))\, u(t), \qquad x(0) = x^0, \qquad (22.1)$$

where $x = (x_1, x_2)$ while u is a scalar-valued measurable control with $|u(t)| \leq 1$. The functions $A_i, B_i, i = 1, 2$, are assumed to be once continuously differentiable in the plane. A solution, for control choice u, which exists (locally) and is unique, will be denoted by $\varphi(t, u, x^0)$. The optimization problem will be to minimize a (cost) functional of the form

$$\int_0^{t_f} L(\varphi(\tau; u, x_0))\, d\tau,$$

where t_f [actually $t_f(u)$] is the smallest nonnegative value of t such that $\varphi(t_f; u, x_0) = x^f$, x^f being a given terminal (target) state. Here L is assumed to be a once continuously differentiable, real-valued function. Of particular interest is the case $L \equiv 1$ which reduces to the time optimal problem.

Before dicussing the problem of obtaining an optimal control, we will determine the region in E^2 in which solution trajectories can exist. Define

$$R(x^0) = \{x \in E^2 : x = \varphi(t, u, x^0),\, t \in [0, \infty),\, u \text{ admissible}\},$$
$$R(x^f) = \{x \in E^2 : x = \varphi(-t, u, x^f),\, t \in [0, \infty),\, u \text{ admissible}\},$$

where $\varphi(-t, u, x_f)$ denotes a solution of

$$\dot{x}_1(t) = -A_1(x(t)) - B_1(x(t))\, u(t),$$
$$\dot{x}_2(t) = -A_2(x(")) - B_2(x(t))\, u(t), \qquad x(0) = x^f.$$

In words, $R(x^0)$ is the set of points which can be attained from x^0, while $R(x^f)$ is the set of points from which x^f can be attained.

Obviously, if a solution to the optimal control problem for (22.1) exists the arc of the trajectory connecting x^0 to x^f must lie in $R(x^0) \cap R(x^f)$. Also, if $R(x^0) \cap R(x^f) \neq \varnothing$, the empty set, there will be an admissible control u with the corresponding solution trajectory joining x^0 and x^f.

Our first goal will be to find a constructive method of determining $R(x^0) \cap R(x^f)$. It will be shown that, with several conditions satisfied. the boundary of this set consists of arcs of the trajectories $\varphi(t, 1, x^0)$, $\varphi(t, -1, x^0)$, $\varphi(-t, 1, x^f)$, and $\varphi(-t, -1, x^f)$.

Let $y \in E^2$, $|\alpha| \leq 1$, and define the vector

$$\xi(\alpha, y) = (A_1(y) + \alpha\, B_1(y),\ A_2(y) + \alpha\, B_2(y)).$$

Then the set of possible "directions" which a solution of (22.1) can assume at the point y is given by $\{\xi(\alpha, y): |\alpha| \leq 1\}$.
Let

$$\Delta(y) = -B_2(y)\, A_1(y) + A_2(y)\, B_1(y). \tag{22.2}$$

Note that $\Delta(y) \neq 0$ implies y is *not* a rest point solution of (22.1) for any admissible control. Define $\theta(\alpha, y)$ to be the angle traced out by the ray $\xi(\sigma, y)$ as σ varies continuously from -1 to α. The angle will be called positive if it is traced out in a counterclockwise direction and negative if in a clockwises direction.

Lemma 22.1 If $\Delta(y) \neq 0$, the set $\{\xi(\alpha, y): |\alpha| \leq 1\}$ of possible directions is bounded by $\xi(-1, y)$ and $\xi(1, y)$ with $0 < |\theta(1, y)| < \pi$.

Proof. For any $-1 \leq \alpha \leq 1$, $\xi(\alpha, y)$ lies on the line segment joining $\xi(-1, y)$ and $\xi(1, y)$, since we can write $\xi(\alpha, y) = ((\alpha + 1)/2)\, \xi(1, y) + ((1 - \alpha)/2)\xi(-1, y)$. Thus $\xi(-1, y)$, $\xi(1, y)$ bound $\{\xi(\alpha, y): |\alpha| \leq 1\}$.

Letting $|\xi(\alpha, y)|$ denote the length of the vector $\xi(\alpha, y)$, the condition $\Delta(y) \neq 0$ implies $|\xi(\alpha, y)| \neq 0$ and that $\xi(-1, y)$ and $\xi(\alpha, y)$ are linearly independent for any $-1 < \alpha \leq 1$, thus $0 < |\theta(1, y)| < \pi$.

In view of this lemma the directions $\xi(1, x^0)$ and $\xi(-1, x^0)$ bound the set of possible directions at x^0, and the angle $\theta(1, x^0)$, which we may assume for the sake of this disucussion to be positive, is such that $0 < \theta(1, x^0) < \pi$. The next lemma will show that if we were to observe the angle $\theta(1, \varphi(t; 1, x^0))$ as t increases from zero, the condition $\Delta(\varphi(t; 1, x^0)) \neq 0$ implies the invariance of the sign of $\theta(1, \varphi(t; -1, x^0))$. Intuitively one would expect that all possible trajectories are restricted to a " wedge-shaped " region bounded by $\varphi(\cdot ; 1, x^0)$ and $\varphi(\cdot ; -1, x^0)$.

Lemma 20.2   Let $\gamma(\sigma)$, $\sigma_0 \leq \sigma \leq \sigma_f$, be a continuous curve in E^2 such that $\Delta(\gamma(\sigma)) \neq 0$. Then sign $\theta(1, \gamma(\sigma))$ is invariant along the curve.

Proof. Since $\theta(1, \gamma(\sigma))$ is a continuous function of σ, if it changes sign there would be a value $\sigma_1 \in [\sigma_0, \sigma_f]$ such that $\theta(1, \gamma(\sigma_1)) = 0$. The assumption $\Delta(\gamma(\sigma)) \neq 0$ and Lemma 22.1 show this cannot happen.

The following example illustrates a case where arcs of the tajectories $\varphi(t, 1, x^0)$, $\varphi(t, -1, x^0)$, $\varphi(-t, 1, x^f)$, and $\varphi(-t, -1, x^f)$ form the boundaries of a compact set S in the plane. Our goal will be to show that, with several conditions satisfied, S is $R(x^0) \cap R(x^f)$.

EXAMPLE 22.1.

$$\dot{x}_1 = x_1{}^2 - x_1{}^2 x_2 u, \qquad x^0 = (1, 0), \quad |u(t)| \leq 1,$$
$$\dot{x}_2 = -x_2 + u, \qquad x^f = (2, 0).$$

Calculation yields (see Fig. 22.1):

$$\varphi(t, 1, x^0) = \begin{cases} \varphi_1(t, 1, x^0) = e^t \\ \varphi_2(t, 1, x^0) = 1 - e^{-t} \end{cases}$$

$$\varphi(t, -1, x^0) = \begin{cases} \varphi_1(t, -1, x^0) = e^t \\ \varphi_2(t, -1, x^0) = e^{-t} - 1 \end{cases}$$

$$\varphi(-t, 1, x^f) = \begin{cases} \dfrac{1}{e^t - 1/2}, \\ 1 - e^t, \end{cases} \qquad \varphi(-t, -1, x^f) = \begin{cases} \dfrac{1}{e^t - 1/2} \\ e^t - 1. \end{cases}$$

Also:

$$\Delta(x) = x_1{}^2 [x_2{}^2 - 1].$$

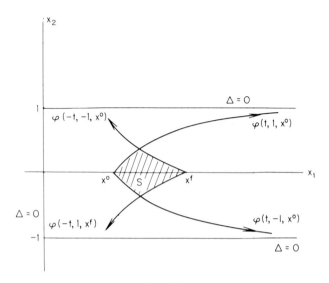

FIG. 22.1.

Our main purpose is to obtain a method for solving a class of control problems which will provide interesting examples. We will require that the examples satisfy the following conditions:

(i) $\varphi(t, 1, x^0)$ and $\varphi(t, -1, x^0)$ have only the point x^0 in common, while $\varphi(-t, 1, x^f)$ and $\varphi(-t, -1, x^f)$ have only the point x^f in common.

(ii) $\varphi(t, 1, x^0)$ and $\varphi(-t, -1, x^f)$ intersect in a unique point other than x^f. Also $\varphi(t, -1, x^0)$ and $\varphi(-t, 1, x^f)$ intersect in a unique point other than x^f.

The above conditions insure that arcs of the trajectories $\varphi(t, 1, x^0)$, $\varphi(t, -1, x^0)$, $\varphi(-t, 1, x^f)$, and $\varphi(-t, -1, x^f)$ form the boundary of a compact region S of the plane having nonempty interior. We require, in addition, that

(iii) $\Delta(x) \neq 0$ for $x \in S$.

With these assumptions, one may conclude that

$$S \subset R(x^0) \cap R(x^f).$$

Indeed, condition (iii) shows that the equation

$$\dot{x}_1 = A_1(x) + B_1(x),$$
$$\dot{x}_2 = A_2(x) + B_2(x)$$

has no rest point solutions in S. Therefore the trajectory $\varphi(t, 1, y)$ must leave S, and in doing so intersect the arc of $\varphi(-t, -1, x^f)$ which contributes to the boundary of S. By switching to control $u = -1$ at the time this intersection occurs, it is easily seen that $y \in R(x^f)$. Similarly, $\varphi(-t, 1, y)$ must intersect the arc of $\varphi(t, -1, x^0)$ which contributes to the boundary of S showing that $y \in R(x^0)$.

Our goal is to obtain conditions which insure $S = R(x^0) \cap R(x^f)$. To accomplish this an additional assumption is needed. Let

$$\Gamma(x^0) = \{\varphi(t, 1, x^0): \ t \geq 0\} \cup \{\varphi(t, -1, x^0): \ t \geq 0\}$$

and

$$\Gamma(x^f) = \{\varphi(-t, 1, x^f): \ t \geq 0\} \cup \{\varphi(-t, -1, x^f): \ t \geq 0\}.$$

If $E^2 - \Gamma(x^0)$ is *not* arcwise connected, we shall say $\Gamma(x^0)$ *separates the plane* and similarly for $\Gamma(x^f)$. If neither $\Gamma(x^0)$ or $\Gamma(x^f)$ separates the plane, one may have a situation as pictured in Fig. 22.2. In this case $S \neq R(x^0) \cap R(x^f)$.

The additional condition is:

(iv) At least one of the arcs $\Gamma(x^0)$ or $\Gamma(x^f)$ separates the plane and $\Delta(x) \neq 0$ for x on the arc that separates.

With Conditions (i)–(iv) satisfied we may show

$$S = R(x^0) \cap R(x^f).$$

Indeed, suppose $\Gamma(x^0)$ separates the plane partitioning it into the arcwise disjoint sets H_1 and H_2. For identification purposes, suppose $x^f \in H_2$. Let y be any point of $E^2 - S$. If $y \in H_1$, Lemma 22.2 can be used to show it is not attainable from x^0 while if $y \in H_2$ or is on $\Gamma(x^0)$ but not in S, x^f is not attainable from y. Thus $R(x^0) \cap R(x^f) \subset S$, and hence these sets are equal.

EXERCISE 22.1. Complete the details of the above discussion.

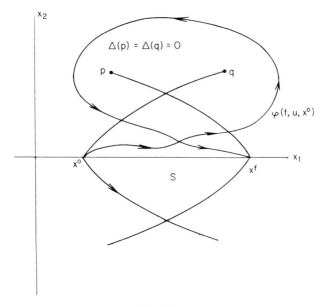

$$\text{FIG. 22.2.}$$

We may note that in Example 22.1, $\Gamma(x^0)$ separates the plane and all of the conditions (i) through (iv) are satisfied. The following are examples which do not satisfy these conditions.

EXAMPLE 22.2.

$$\dot{x}_1 = x_1 + x_2 u, \qquad |u(t)| \leq 1,$$
$$\dot{x}_2 = x_2 + x_1 u, \qquad x^0 = (2, 0), \quad x^f = (1, 0).$$

Then (see Fig. 22.3):

$$\varphi(t; 1, x^0) = \begin{cases} e^{2t} + 1, \\ e^{2t} - 1, \end{cases} \qquad\qquad \varphi(t; -1, x^0) = \begin{cases} e^{2t} + 1, \\ 1 - e^{2t}, \end{cases}$$

$$\varphi(-t; 1, x^f) = \begin{cases} \tfrac{1}{2}(e^{-2t} + 1) \\ \tfrac{1}{2}(e^{-2t} - 1), \end{cases} \qquad \varphi(-t; -1, x^f) = \begin{cases} \tfrac{1}{2}(e^{-2t} + 1) \\ \tfrac{1}{2}(1 - e^{-2t}), \end{cases}$$

while $\Delta(x) = x_2{}^2 - x_1{}^2$.

EXERCISE 22.2. Examine the region $R(x^f)$ more carefully; i.e., describe it completely.

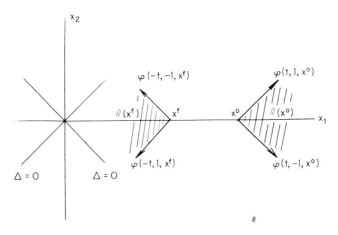

FIG. 22.3.

EXAMPLE 22.3. In this example (see Fig. 22.4) only a possible configuration will be shown, rather than derive the situation as an example from a set of differential equations. One should note that the example does not violate either Lemma 22.1 or Lemma 2.22, even if the corresponding $\Delta(x)$ is zero only at the origin.

Note that although $\varphi(\cdot, 1, x^0)$ intersects $\varphi(\cdot, -1, x^0)$ several times, the sign of $\theta(1, \varphi(\cdot, -1, x^0))$ remains the same at these points of intersection.

EXERCISE 22.3. Show that a picture such as in Fig. 22.4 could not be obtained if $\Delta(x) \neq 0$ for all $x \in E^2$. Describe $R(x^0)$ for Fig. 22.4.

Rather than try to specify the most general conditions which lead to problems with Properties (i)–(iv), we assume the properties and will check each example individually. This completes, for the moment, the discussion of the admissible region $R(x^0) \cap R(x^f)$. We will next proceed to the determination of optimal controls.

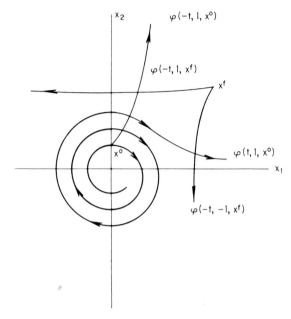

FIG. 22.4.

Synthesis by Green's Theorem

Let $\Delta(x) \neq 0$ for $x \in R(x^0) \cap R(x^f)$ and $\{\varphi(t, u, p): t_p(u) \leq t \leq t_q(u)\}$ be an arc of an admissible trajectory of (22.1) connecting two points p and q in $R(x^0) \cap R(x^f)$; i.e., $\varphi(t_p, u, p) = p$ while $\varphi(t_q, u, p) = q$. The cost functional can be expressed as a line integral along this arc by multiplying the first of Eqs. (22.1) by $-L(x) B_2(x)$, the second by $L(x) B_1(x)$, adding, and dividing by $\Delta(x)$ to obtain

$$\int_{t_p}^{t_q} L(\varphi(\tau, u, p)) \, d\tau = \int_p^q -\frac{LB_2}{\Delta} \, dx_1 + \frac{LB_1}{\Delta} \, dx_2,$$

where the line integral is taken along the arc of $\varphi(t, u, p)$ joining p to q.

Now suppose $\varphi(t, u_1, p)$ and $\varphi(t, u_2, p)$ are two different solutions of (3.3.1), each joining p to q in $R(x^0) \cap R(x^f)$ and having no points other than p and q in common. Let Γ be the closed curve formed by these trajectory arcs. Assume we traverse Γ in a counterclockwise fashion by following first the arc of $\varphi(t, u_1, p)$ from p to q and next the arc of $\varphi(t, u_2, p)$ from q to p. Denoting

$$C(u_i, p, q) = \int_{t_p(u_i)}^{t_q(u_i)} L(\varphi(\tau, u_i, p)) \, d\tau$$

one finds

$$C(u_1, p, q) - C(u_2, p, q) = \oint_\Gamma -\frac{LB_2}{\Delta} \, dx_1 + \frac{LB_1}{\Delta} \, dx_2.$$

Since the bounding curve Γ is a Jordan arc, applying Green's theorem to the above yields

$$C(u_1, p, q) - C(u_2, p, q) = \iint_{\mathcal{R}} \omega(x) \, ds, \qquad (22.3)$$

where

$$\omega(x) = \frac{\partial}{\partial x_1} \left(\frac{LB_1}{\Delta}\right) + \frac{\partial}{\partial x_2} \left(\frac{LB_2}{\Delta}\right)$$

and $\mathcal{R}$ is the region enclosed by Γ.

Since $\omega(x)$ can be computed without knowledge of a solution of the differential equations (22.1), this provides a *direct* method for comparing the relative optimality of two trajectories by examining the sign of ω in the region they enclose.

EXAMPLE 22.4.

$$\dot{x}_1 = 1 + x_2 u, \qquad x^0 = (0, 2), \quad |u(t)| \le 1,$$
$$\dot{x}_2 = x_2 - u, \qquad x^f = (0, 3).$$

Problem: minimize $\int_0^{t_f} 1 \, d\tau$, i.e., time optimal.

$$\Delta(x) \equiv 1 + x_2^2$$

$$\omega(x) = \frac{\partial}{\partial x_1} \left(\frac{x_2}{1 + x_2^2}\right) + \frac{\partial}{\partial x_2} \left(\frac{-1}{1 + x_2^2}\right) = \frac{2x_2}{(1 + x_2^2)^2}.$$

Let C_1 be any arc joining x^0 to x^f in $R(x^0) \cap R(x^f)$ and C_2 be the arc composed of the trajectories $\varphi(t; -1, x^0)$ and $\varphi(-t; 1, x^f)$ as shown in Fig. 22.5.

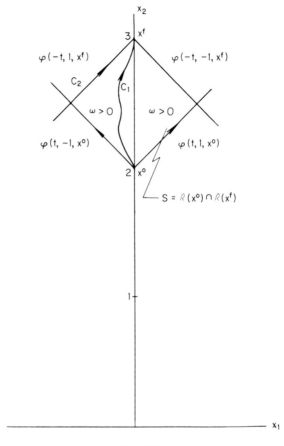

FIG. 22.5.

Since $\omega(x) > 0$ in $R(x^0) \cap R(x^f)$ one finds that the cost along curve C_1 minus the cost along C_2 is positive; i.e., curve C_2 is "better" than C_1. This is true for any admissible trajectory arc C_1; i.e., C_2 is the optimal arc.

Before we discuss more examples, let us examine more closely the reasoning behind the Green theorem approach.

A *homeomorphism f* of a topological space X into a topological space Y is a one-to-one continuous map having a continuous inverse.

An *arc* in a topological space Y is a homeomorphic image of a closed real interval. A *path* φ is a continuous mapping of a closed real interval into Y; the image in Y of φ is called the *track* or orbit of φ. Clearly, a track may have self-intersections, an arc may not. It is evident that by changing parametrization, two different paths may have the same track.

In the Green theorem approach, the idea is motivated by considering two paths which are admissible solutions of the differential equations and whose tracks join given points p and q and have only these points in common. The merit of the idea lies in the fact that it is a direct method; i.e., it leads to comparing the relative optimality of trajectories without explicitly computing the solutions of the differential equations. Specifically, one uses (22.3) to obtain the optimal arc in $R(x^0) \cap R(x^f)$. In order that this lead to a useful result, we must show:

Lemma 22.3 If Γ is an arc in $R(x^0) \cap R(x^f)$ which may be realized as the track of a solution of (22.1) and if $\Delta(x) \neq 0$ for $x \in \Gamma$, then the control u leading to the solution with track Γ is uniquely determined to within a set of zero measure (i.e., the solution (path) of (22.1) having Γ as its track is unique).

Proof. Let $\varphi(t, u)$, $0 \leq t \leq t_1$, be a solution of (22.1) with control u and having track Γ. Now $\Delta(\varphi(t, u)) \neq 0$ implies $|\dot{\varphi}(t, u)| \neq 0$, and since Γ is an arc (has no self-intersections) it follows that $\varphi(t, u)$ is a homeomorphism. Suppose $\varphi(\sigma, v)$, $0 \leq \sigma \leq \sigma_1$, is also a solution with control v and having track Γ. Define a map $h : [0, t_1] \to [0, \sigma_1]$ by $\varphi(h(t), v) = \varphi(t, u)$. Then h is a homeomorphism and therefore must be monotone since it maps a real interval onto a real interval. We may assume $h(0) = 0$. Now a monotone map has a derivative almost everywhere, but need *not* be absolutely continuous. At a later point, we shall need the formula $\int_0^t h'(\tau)\, d\tau = h(t)$; hence we next will compute h explicitly and show that it is absolutely continuous.

The arc length of the segment of Γ between the points $\varphi(0, u)$ and $\varphi(t, u)$ is given by $s(t) = \int_0^t \{\sum_1^n \dot{\varphi}_i^2(\tau, u)\}^{1/2}\, d\tau = \int_0^t |\dot{\varphi}(\tau, u)|\, d\tau$. Similarly, the arc length between the points $\varphi(0, v)$ and $\varphi(\sigma, v)$ is given by $l(\sigma) = \int_0^\sigma |\dot{\varphi}(\tau, v)|\, d\tau$. From the continuity conditions on the right side of (22.1), there exists an $M > 0$ such that $|\dot{\varphi}(\sigma, v)| \leq M$ for $0 \leq \sigma \leq \sigma_1$. On the other hand, the hypothesis $\Delta(\varphi(\sigma, v)) \neq 0$ for $0 \leq \sigma \leq \sigma_1$ yields the existence of an $m > 0$ such that $|\dot{\varphi}(\sigma, v)| \geq m$ for $0 \leq \sigma \leq \sigma_1$. It follows that $l(\sigma)$ is a Lipschitz continuous function with a Lipschitz continuous inverse which we shall denote l^{-1}. From its representation, $s(t)$ is absolutely continuous. By "matching arc length" one sees that if $\sigma = l^{-1}(s(t))$ then $\varphi(\sigma, v) = \varphi(t, u)$. Thus the required function h is given by $h(t) = l^{-1}(s(t))$ and is the composite of a Lipschitz continuous function with an absolutely continuous function, hence is absolutely continuous. [Actually $s(t)$ is also Lipschitz continuous.]

Differentiating the identity $\varphi(h(t), v) = \varphi(t, u)$ with respect to t yields $h(t)\varphi'(h(t), v) = \dot{\varphi}(t, u)$ or

$$h(t)\begin{bmatrix} A_1(\varphi(h(t), v)) & B_1(\varphi(h(t), v)) \\ A_2(\varphi(h(t), v)) & B_2(\varphi(h(t), v)) \end{bmatrix}\begin{bmatrix} 1 \\ v(h(t)) \end{bmatrix}$$

$$= \begin{bmatrix} A_1(\varphi(t, u)) & B_1(\varphi(t, u)) \\ A_2(\varphi(t, u)) & B_2(\varphi(t, u)) \end{bmatrix}\begin{bmatrix} 1 \\ u(t) \end{bmatrix}$$

for almost all $t \in [0, t_1]$. Since $\varphi(h(t), v) = \varphi(t, u)$ and $\Delta(x) \neq 0$ implies the matrix is nonsingular, we conclude $\dot{h}(t) = 1$ and $v(h(t)) = u(t)$. But h is absolutely continuous, $h(0) = 0$, hence $h(t) = t$ and $v(h(t)) = v(t) = u(t)$ almost everywhere, completing the proof.

To summarize, the procedure in the use of the Green's theorem approach is as follows. First compute $\Delta(x)$ and determine $R(x^0) \cap R(x^f)$. If $\Delta x \neq 0$ in $R(x^0) \cap R(x^f)$, $\omega(x)$ can be computed and its algebraic sign can be used to determine the optimal arc joining x^0 of x^f in $R(x^0) \cap R(x^f)$. If this arc is realizable as the track of a solution of (22.1), the control producing a solution with this track is unique and optimal. The problem of whether or not the optimal arc in $R(x^0) \cap R(x^f)$ is realziable as the track of a solution depends on the zeros of $\omega(x)$. This is best seen by the following example:

EXAMPLE 22.5. Consider

$$\begin{aligned} \dot{x}_1(t) &= x_1(t) + x_2(t)\, u(t), & x^0 &= (1, 0), \\ \dot{x}_2(t) &= x_2(t) + x_1(t)\, u(t), & x^f &= (3, 0), \end{aligned} \tag{22.4}$$

with $|u(t)| \leq 1$ and the problem being to minimize $\int_0^{t_f} L(x(\tau))\, d\tau$, where $L(x) = x_1 + bx_2 - 2b \ln(x_1 + x_2)$. Then

$$\omega(x) = \frac{-x_2 - bx_1 + 2b}{x_1{}^2 - x_2{}^2}$$

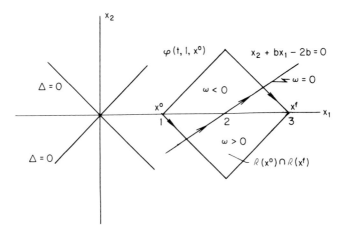

FIG. 22.6.

while $\Delta(x) = x_2{}^2 - x_1{}^2$, and the region $R(x^0) \cap R(x^f)$ is as pictured in Fig. 22.6.

We consider first $-1 \le b \le 1$. In this case the arc $\omega = 0$ can be realized as a trajectory for the system (22.4). By comparison of arcs, one concludes the optimal track is as shown by the arrows in Fig. 22.6. If $|b| < 1$, then $|u(t)| < 1$ along the part of the trajectory which has $\{x: \omega(x) = 0\}$ as its track. If $b = 1$, this arc is realized with the control u satisfying $|u(t)| = 1$. If $|b| > 1$, there is no control, satisfying $|u(t)| \le 1$, which leads to a trajectory having a track coinciding with $\{x: \omega(x) = 0\}$. This is the case where the zeros of ω are such that the optimal arc is not realizable as a track of an admissible solution and the method is inconclusive.

EXAMPLE 22.6. Consider Eqs. (22.4) with initial and terminal data as in Example 22.5 but the problem being the time optimal problem. Then $L \equiv 1$, $\Delta(x)$ and $R(x^0) \cap R(x^f)$ are as in Example 22.5, but $\omega(x) \equiv 0$. Equation (22.3) shows that the difference in cost along any two admissible trajectories joining x^0 and x^f is zero; i.e., the problem is independent of control. Indeed, by multiplying the first of Eqs. (22.4) by x_1 the second by $-x_2$, and adding, one obtains $x_1 \dot{x}_1 - x_2 \dot{x}_2 = x_1{}^2 - x_2{}^2$; hence all solutions satisfy $x_1{}^2(t) + x_2{}^2(t) = e^{2t}$. From this

it is easily seen that the time necessary to reach x^f is indeed independent
of control..

EXAMPLE 22.7   (A time optimal problem in which the optimal control
is *not* bang-bang). Consider the time optimal problem for the equations
and initial and final data in Example 22.1. The set $R(x^0) \cap R(x^f)$ is
given in Fig. 22.1. Then $\omega(x) = -2x_2/x_1^2[1 - x_2^2]^2$, and one concludes
that the optimal arc is

$$\{(x_1, x_2): x_2 = 0, 1 \leq x_1 \leq 2\},$$

i.e., an arc along which $\omega = 0$. It is easily seen that the control which
yields the optimal trajectory is $u \equiv 0$. In view of Lemma 22.3, this
control is unique to within a set of measure zero. Therefore this is an
example of a time optimal problem for a system with control appearing
linearly, yet the optimal time is not attainable by a bang-bang control.

EXERCISE 22.4. Show that for any two-dimensional system of the
form (22.1) there exists a function $L(x)$ so that minimizing $\int_0^{t_f} L(x(\tau)) \, d\tau$
is independent of control.

Hint: Any two-dimensional pfaffian has an integrating factor.

EXAMPLE 22.8   (The Goddard rocket problem). Consider a small
rocket fired vertically from the surface of the earth. Assume that the
initial mass of the rocket and fuel is m_0, while when all fuel is used up
the rocket has mass m^f. It is assumed that the rocket is a variable thrust
vehicle, with thrust T satisfying $0 \leq T(t) \leq 1$. The problem is to utilize
thrust as a function of time subject to its constraints, in such a way as to
attain maximum height.
    The rocket equation is

$$(v - v_e) \, dm + (m - dm)(v + dv) - mv = F \, dt,$$

where v is rocket velocity, v_e the gas escape velocity, and F the forces
acting. In a constant atmosphere and constant gravitational field, an
approximate F is $F = -kv^2 - mg$, k a constant while g is the gravity
constant. Then

$$m \frac{dv}{dt} - v_e \frac{dm}{dt} = -kv^2 - mg.$$

Now $m(t) = m_0 - \int_0^t T(\tau) \, d\tau$, yielding the system

$$\frac{dv}{dt} = -\frac{kv^2}{m} - g - \frac{v_e}{m} T(t)$$

$$\frac{dm}{dt} = -T(t), \qquad v = \frac{dh}{dt},$$

where h will designate height. The conditions are clearly $v(t_f) = 0$, $v(0) = 0$, $h(0) = 0$, $m(t_f) = m_f$, $m(0) = m_0$.

Changing to h as independent variable,

$$\frac{dv}{dt} = \frac{dv}{dh}\frac{dh}{dt} = \frac{dv}{dh} v, \qquad \frac{dm}{dt} = v \frac{dm}{dh},$$

and we now seek a feedback optimal thrust $T(m, v)$. The equations of motion become

$$v \frac{dv}{dh} = -\frac{kv^2}{m} - g - \frac{v_e T}{m}, \qquad v(0) = v(h_f) = 0$$

$$v \frac{dm}{dh} = -T, \qquad\qquad m(0) = m_0, \quad m(h_f) = m_f,$$

with the problem being to *maximize* $\int_0^{h_f} 1 \, dh$ with the control constrained by $0 \leq T \leq 1$. Utilizing the Green theorem approach,

$$v \, dv - \frac{vv_e}{m} \, dm = \left(-\frac{kv^2}{m} - g \right) dh,$$

and since $(-kv^2/m - g) \neq 0$, $\Delta(v, m) \neq 0$. Also a computation gives

$$\omega(v, m) = \frac{-kv^2 v_e + gmv_e + kv^3}{(kv^2 + mg)^2}.$$

The region of interest is as shown in Fig. 22.7.

Depending on the values of constants present in the equations of motion, the following situations may occur: (i) The curve $\omega = 0$ lies to the right of the region of interest in Fig. 22.7. In this case the optimal strategy is full thrust until all fuel is expended, after which there will be a coasting arc with $T = 0$. (ii) The cruve $\omega = 0$ intersects the region of interest and is realizable as the track of a trajectory. In this case the

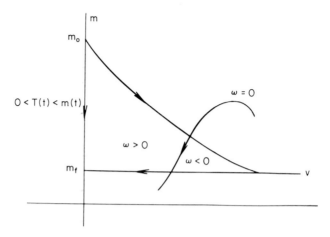

FIG. 22.7.

optimal strategy is full thrust to begin with, then a "programmed" or intermediate thrust arc (which follows $\omega = 0$), and finally the coast arc. (iii) The curve $\omega = 0$ intersects the region of interest but is not realizable as the track of an admissible trajectory. Here the Green theorem approach does not apply directly and a more detailed analysis is necessary.

23. A Further Look at the Maximum Principle and Singular Arcs

We next state, without proof, the maximum principle for a time optimal, point-to-point transfer problem with system equations

$$\dot{x}(t) = f(t, x(t), u(t)).$$

Here $x = (x_1, \ldots, x_n)$, $u = (u_1, \ldots, u_r)$, with an admissible control being a measurable function with values in a compact set U. We shall assume that f is continuously differentiable in all arguments. Define

$$H(t, x, p, u) = p \cdot f(t, x, u) - p_0$$
$$H^*(t, x, p) = \max\{H(t, x, p, u): u \in U\}.$$

Maximum Principle

A necessary condition that u^* is an optimal control and $\varphi(t, u^*)$ the corresponding optimal trajectory is that there exists a nonzero vector function $p = (p_1, \ldots, p_n)$ such that

$$H(t, \varphi(t, u^*), p(t), u^*(t)) \equiv H^*(t, \varphi(t, u^*), p(t))$$

and

$$\dot{p}(t) = -\frac{\partial}{\partial x} H(t, \varphi(t, u^*), p(t), u^*(t)) = -\frac{\partial}{\partial x} H^*(t, \varphi(t, u^*), p(t)).$$

Transversality

We are particularly interested in the case when f is independent of time, i.e., $f(x, u)$, in which case the transversality condition becomes

$$H^*(\varphi(t, u^*), p(t)) \equiv p_0 \geq 0 \qquad \text{in} \quad t.$$

REMARK. The maximum principle is a necessary condition, similar to the Euler–Lagrange equations and Weierstrass condition of the calculus of variations. It may be considered as a linear (and second-order) approximation or "derivative" test, for seeking a maximum or minimum of a functional defined on the path space of a control system. In analogy, if we seek a maximum of a real-valued function f of a single real variable x, the fact that $f'(x_0) = 0$ and $f''(x_0) \leq 0$ does not alone imply x_0 provides f a local maximum. These are, however, necessary conditions. In a similar way, the maximum principle includes only the first- and second-order approximations. It is easy to construct a real-valued function of a real variable with an inflection point at zero, but for which all derviatives at zero vanish. For example,

$$f(x) = \begin{cases} e^{-1/x^2}, & x > 0, \\ 0, & x = 0, \\ -e^{-1/x^2}, & x < 0 \end{cases}$$

has this property.

The behavior of f in a neighborhood of zero cannot be determined by derivatives, no matter how high an order we consider. An analogous example can be constructed for a functional (cost functional) defined on the path space of a control system. Problems in which the maximum principle yields no constructive information are termed singular problems. These may intuitively be considered as cases where a third- or higher-order test would be needed to determine the behavior of the cost functional in a neighborhood of an "extremal" path, i.e., one which satisfies the maximum principle. Our method for analyzing these problems, *in two dimensions*, will again be by the Green theorem, which is a global approach to minimization, i.e., does not depend on local approximations as does the maximum principle. Although there is not complete agreement on definitions of singular arcs, that which we shall next give is the most common.

SINGULAR SOLUTIONS

If the maximum principle is applied to a time optimal problem with system equations 22.1, one finds

$$H(t, x, p, u) = p_1 A_1(x) + p_2 A_2(x) + [p_1 B_1(x) + p_2 B_2(x)]u - 1.$$

If u is restricted to take values between -1 and 1, the maximum principle implies an optimal control u^* must satisfy

$$u^*(t) = \operatorname{sgn}[p_1(t) B_1(\varphi(t, u^*)) + p_2(t) B_2(\varphi(t, u^*))].$$

However, it is possible that the quantity inside the brackets can be identically zero for a set of values t having positive measure, in which case the maximum principle yields no information as to the value $u^*(t)$.

Now let u be any admissible control, and $\varphi(t, u)$ the corresponding solution of (22.1). Define $H(t, x, p, u)$ as above. If there exists a nonzero vector-valued function p which satisfies the differential equation

$$\dot{p}(t) = -\frac{\partial}{\partial x} H(t, \varphi(t, u), p(t), u(t))$$

and yields

$$[p_1(t) B_1(\varphi(t, u)) + p_2(t) B_2(\varphi(t, u))] \equiv 0 \qquad (23.1)$$

for $t \in I$, a set of positive measure, then the restriction of φ to I is called a *singular solution*. Singular solutions are of much mathematical interest because of the number of necessary conditions they automatically satisfy, yet are not necessarily optimal.

EXERCISE 23.1. Show that if $\varphi(t, u)$ is a singular solution of (22.1) along which $\Delta \neq 0$, then $\omega(\varphi(t, u)) \equiv 0$.

EXERCISE 23.2. Show directly (not using $\omega = 0$) that the solution of Example 22.7 is a singular solution.

EXERCISE 23.3. Show that $u \equiv 0$ yields a singular solution in the time optimal problem for

$$\dot{x}_1(t) = u \qquad\qquad x^0 = (0, 0),$$
$$\dot{x}_2(t) = 1 + x_2 x_1{}^2 u, \qquad x^f = (0, \tfrac{1}{2})$$

with $|u(t)| \leq 1$. Use the Green theorem method to show that this solution is *not* optimal. [Actually, it provides neither a maximum nor a minimum, but is equivalent to an inflection point in the path space, for the functional $t_f(u)$. If the second equation is replaced by $\dot{x}_2 = 1 + x_2 x_1^{2n} u$, the "flatness" of the inflection point increases with n. If it is replaced by $\dot{x}_2 = 1 + x_2[\exp(-1/x_1{}^2)]u$, it is an inflection point which cannot be determined by any number of derivatives.]

EXERCISE 23.4. The nonlinear system (22.1) is said to be *locally controllable* along the solution $\varphi(t, u)$ if for some $t_1 > 0$ all points in some neighborhood of $\varphi(t_1, u)$ are attainable by trajectories of (22.1) with admissible controls.

(a) Show that a sufficient condition for (22.1) to be locally controllable along the solution $\varphi(t, u)$, where $|u(t)| < 1$, is that the linear variational equation associated with φ is controllable; that is, letting

$$A(x) = \begin{pmatrix} A_1(x) \\ A_2(x) \end{pmatrix}, \qquad B(x) = \begin{pmatrix} B_1(x) \\ B_2(x) \end{pmatrix},$$

and $A_x(x)$, $B_x(x)$ be the matrices of partial derivatives, show that a sufficient condition is that the variational equation

$$\dot{y}(t) = [A_x(\varphi(t, u)) + B_x(\varphi(t, u)) u(t)] y(t) + B(\varphi(t, u)) v(t)$$

is controllable.

(b) Assume that A and B are analytic. Show that if $\varphi(t, u)$ is an analytic singular solution of (22.1), the associated variational equation (of Part a) is *not* controllable.

Note: This does *not* mean that (22.1) is not locally controllable along the singular solution, but only that the most obvious sufficient condition fails. In fact, Exercise 23.3 provides a singular solution along which the system is locally controllable.

References*

1. Liapunov, A., Sur les fonctions-vecteurs completement additives, *Bull. Acad. Sci. USSR, Ser. Math.* **4**, 465–478 (1940).
2. Lindenstrauss, J., A short proof of Liapunoff's convexity theorem, *J. Math. Mech.* **15**, (6), 971–972 (1966).
3. Richter, H., Verallgemeinerung eines in der Statistik benötigten Satzes der Masstheorie, *Math. Ann.* **150**, 85–90, 440–441 (1963).
4. Aumann, R. J., Integrals of set-valued functions, *J. Math. Anal. Appl.* **12** 1–12, (1965).
5. Eggleston, H. G., "Convexity." Cambridge Univ. Press, New York and London, 1958.
6. Plis', A., Remark on measurable set-valued functions, *Bull. Acad. Polon. Sci. Ser. Sci. Math. Astr. et Phy.* **9** (12), 857–859 (1961).
7. Filippov, A. F., On certain questions in the theory of optimal control, *SIAM J. Control* **1**, (1), 76–84 (1962).
8. Bushaw, D., Optimal discontinuous forcing terms, in "Theory of Non-Linear Oscillations," Vol. 4, pp. 29–52. Princeton Univ. Press, Princeton, New Jersey, 1958.
9. LaSalle, J. P., The time optimal control problem, in "Theory of Non-Linear Oscillations," Vol. 5, pp. 1–24. Princeton Univ. Press, Princeton, New Jersey, 1959.

* For extensive bibliographies of past and current research in control theory, the reader is referred to Refs. [12] and [13].

10. Pontryagin, L. S., Boltyanskii, V. G., Gamkrelidze, R. V., and Mishchenko, E. F., "The Mathematical Theory of Optimal Processes." Wiley (Interscience), New York, 1962.
11. Olech, C., Extermal Solutions of a Control System, *J. Diff. Eqs.* **2** (1), 74–101 (1966).
12. Lee, E. B. and Markus, L., "Foundations of Optimal Control Theory." Wiley, New York, 1967.
13. Athans, M., and Falb, P. L., "Optimal Control: An Introduction to the Theory and its Applications." McGraw-Hill, New York, 1965.

Subject Index

Mathematics in Science and Engineering

A Series of Monographs and Textbooks

Edited by RICHARD BELLMAN, *University of Southern California*